THE TEES NEWPORT BRIDGE

The Untold Story of a Steel River Landmark

Heritage
Unl🔒cked

Tosh Warwick

About the Author

Dr Tosh Warwick is a historian and heritage consultant with Heritage Unlocked and Research Associate in Urban Studies at the University of Sheffield. He has appeared as an expert contributor for BBC Television including on *Match of the Day 2*, *Great British Railway Journeys* and *Great Coastal Railway Journeys*, as well as for BBC Radio, Channel 4 News and Channel 5. He is author of a number of books on Teesside's history including *Central Middlesbrough Through Time* (2013), *Memories of Middlesbrough in the 1970s and 1980s* (2020), *Memories of Mannion: South Bank's Golden Boy* (2020), *Memories of Stockton-on-Tees in the 1970s and 1980s* (2021), *Historic Middlesbrough* (2022), *Last Orders! Middlesbrough's Lost & Historic Pubs* (2023), *Memories of Middlesbrough in the 1950s and 1960s* (2024) and is co-author of *River Tees: From Source to Sea* (2016).

Cover Photo: Richard Wagner, Wagner Photographic

Copyright © 2024, Tosh Warwick

ISBN 978-1-7384690-1-7

Typesetting and design by Ben Higgins Graphic Design.

www.heritageunlocked.com

Contents

Acknowledgements

This celebration of the Tees Newport Bridge has been made possible by a range of individuals and organisations that have helped ensure the history and heritage of the Tees Newport Bridge survives into the twenty-first century. Middlesbrough Libraries and Teesside Archives have made accessible their fantastic collections and have been as helpful as ever with various research enquiries and requests for help during numerous visits over the years. Back in 2014 when I first started working towards writing a book about the Newport Bridge, the assistance of Teesside University graduate Jonathon Hooton in patiently sifting through, cataloguing and digitising dozens of documents relating to the bridge has played a vital role in the book coming to fruition. I would also like to recognise the University of Sheffield for supporting my research and writing of this book. I am particularly grateful to Bill Scott OBE DL at Wilton Engineering for his support both for this publication and the work of Heritage Unlocked.

The staff at *The Gazette*, and in particular John Rogan, have been invaluable in providing access to historical material and allowing reproduction of articles and photographs from their archives, many of which have not been seen for many decades. A number of other individuals have been very generous in sharing their knowledge, memories and own personal collections relating to the Newport Bridge. I would like to thank John Severs for sharing his unique photographs that capture Teesside's industrial landmarks and the impact of deindustrialisation during decades of significant change. Robin Dale's images of Newport in the 1970s are reproduced here with the assistance of the Mary Evans Picture Library for which I am very grateful. Robin's work reflects his foresight in committing to film precious snapshots of life largely absent from publicity material, regeneration literature or official records found in more traditional collections from the era. As with a number of my previous publications, material from the late Paul Stephenson's Collection once again helps share the history of Teesside as so many of his works did over the decades. I would also like to thank all the artists who have allowed reproduction of their work in this book, as well as all of those people who have shared memories and provided assistance in research carried out for this book. Finally, I would like to dedicate this book to my five-month-old daughter Abigail, who has already paid a visit to the Dorman Long landmark.

Tosh Warwick, May 2024

Introduction: a Dorman Long Icon and Teesside Landmark

On 28th February 1934 the Duke of York officially opened the Tees (Newport) Bridge as the latest structure built by Dorman Long. Hailed as the 'Tees Wonder Bridge' on the front page of the *North Eastern Daily Gazette*, the new crossing - referred to hereafter interchangeably as the Tees Newport Bridge, Tees Bridge and Newport Bridge given the variety of styles used to refer to the structure - was the subject of national and international interest as the largest vertical-lift bridge of its type in the world. A remarkable feat of engineering that achieved the basic function of spanning the Tees in the most ingenious of ways, the Newport Bridge has played a major role in the economic and transport history of Teesside and continues to fulfil that all-important role of traversing what Chris Rea dubbed the 'Steel River'.

A scene from the opening ceremony in 1934 (Middlesbrough Libraries)

The decline of large shipping from Stockton to the mouth of the Tees resulting from deindustrialisation along with the diversification of industries along the river ultimately rendered the need to elevate the structure redundant. Despite the last lift taking place in 1990, the Newport Bridge remains a symbol of the area's industrial heritage and an ode to the prowess of the area's steelmaking and bridgebuilding history, and in particular that of Dorman Long who built famous bridges across the globe including the Sydney Harbour and Tyne Bridges. It is both a source of pride and curiosity for Teessiders from across the generations, and for some also a subject of frustration and even terror!

As a child I was terrified of the Newport Bridge, believing the Tees steel giant to be some sort of character from Transformers. My experiences of travel sickness travelling to and from Stockton with my Mam during which we would either cross or pass the green monster probably added to the terror! Since then, like many Teessiders, I have developed a passion for the area's history and heritage. Whilst studying for my doctorate I enjoyed a placement with the British Steel Archive Project and Teesside Archives where I discovered a number of records relating to the Newport Bridge detailing the role of Dorman Long in building the bridge and the little known debates around building the crossing. As someone born in Middlesbrough who grew up in South Bank, I had an interest in bridges and with a grandfather who had worked at Dorman Long – the firm whose name was emblazoned on an iconic coal bunker less than a mile from my childhood home – I was hooked. The material inspired an article on the politics of bridge building, several talks and further collaborations with Teesside Archives on the area's bridge building heritage, including work on the Cleveland Bridge Collection.

Whilst working on the Tees Transporter Bridge Visitor Experience Project in 2014, one of the collaborations with Teesside Archives uncovered photographs dating from the early 1930s showing the vertical-lift bridge under construction and the opening ceremony. The same year, the 80th anniversary of the Bridge's opening, I decided that I would write a book about Newport Bridge but other priorities got in the way and years passed before there was any progress – much like the delays from the initial proposals for a new crossing of the Tees to the fruition of the project on that celebrated day in 1934! With the Newport Bridge having celebrated its 90th birthday in February 2024, now seemed an opportune moment to finally finish the book on this sometimes overlooked landmark.

Few publications have been dedicated to the history and heritage of the Tees (Newport) Bridge, with the attention of historians tending to be directed towards its older, peculiar and more famous if troubled Transporter Bridge neighbour. Yet, the Newport crossing has arguably played as significant a role in the economic, cultural and social history of the Tees, Teesside and Teessiders as the 'Tranny'.

Illuminated in red - a modern day photograph of the landmark (Stockton-on-Tees Borough Council)

This book aims to shed new light on not just the history of the Newport Bridge but also the economic, political, social and transport history of industrial Teesside. Beginning by providing an overview of some of the ways the challenge of crossing the Tees has been tackled over the centuries, this book then turns attention to the question of bridging the river at Middlesbrough. The economic challenges and new developments of the interwar era and associated debates around a new crossing of the river are then explored. The complexities of building the new bridge and the significant changes this brought to the Teesside skyline are revealed in the next chapter through previously unpublished photographs and a delve into historic newspaper reports. The Royal Visit for the opening of the Newport Bridge in 1934 is then chronicled in detail alongside many previously unpublished photographs from Teesside's 'red letter day', before the pros and cons of possessing such a novel bridge are highlighted. The Second World War and the post-war decades brought new problems for Teesside and the Newport Bridge and these turbulent times are explored through oral histories and tales from the local press. The changing face of industrial Teesside from in the 1970s and 1980s and the implications for the Dorman Long landmark are charted before the book's penultimate chapter reflects on life after the final lift of the main span and the Bridge's continued importance to Teesside's identity and industrial heritage. The book finishes by sharing memories of Newport Bridge shared by dozens of people, spanning childhood and family connections, working life and how the engineering marvel has inspired artists to celebrate this world-leading bridge that was manufactured on Teesside, constructed on Teesside and has served Teesside for over 90 years.

I hope that this book will not only encourage others to research the area's history and built heritage and make use of incredible local archival and library resources but also encourage new or heightened appreciation of the 'other', less famous bridge spanning the Tees at Middlesbrough.

Crossing the Tees Through Time

"Middlesbrough possessed only one link across the River Tees with County Durham in the Transporter Bridge prior to the construction of the new Tees (Newport) Bridge. On the Transporter Bridge all traffic is carried over the river by a moving car. The Bridge thus at times causes considerable delay to road traffic, is a toll bridge, and has a limited capacity."

Tees Newport Bridge: Official Souvenir Programme, 1934

The issue of crossing the Tees has proven a challenge for millennia and has been met with a variety of solutions by Romans, rowing boats and riveters. In fact, the question of improving communication across the Tees remains a major issue for twenty-first century Teessiders just as it concerned their ancestors. It is not the intention here to reflect on all the approaches to traversing the Tees – there are other excellent books on the topic - but rather to outline some of the ways in which the challenge has been met around Middlesbrough and Stockton-on-Tees.

Fords, tugs and a proposed 'flying ferry'

Long before the opening of the Newport Bridge, those crossing the river in bygone eras used an array of fords, primitive boat systems, row ferries, crowded tugs and a 'flying ferry' to make the journey.

Middlesbrough in the 1830s (Middlesbrough Libraries)

Middlesbrough developed as a coal export town in the 1830s as a result of the extension of the Stockton & Darlington Railway to the hamlet on the south bank of the Tees in 1830 at Port Darlington – on the site of Port of Middlesbrough a stone's throw from the Transporter Bridge today. The extension of the railway included the construction of a suspension bridge (1830) at Stockton that helped connect the railway to Middlesbrough but the design proved unsuitable for railway traffic as the structure perilously swayed erratically and had to propped up to make it useable until an iron-trussed structure replaced it in 1844.

An early sketch of the coal staithes at Port Darlington

The Stockton & Darlington Railway Suspension Bridge over the Tees

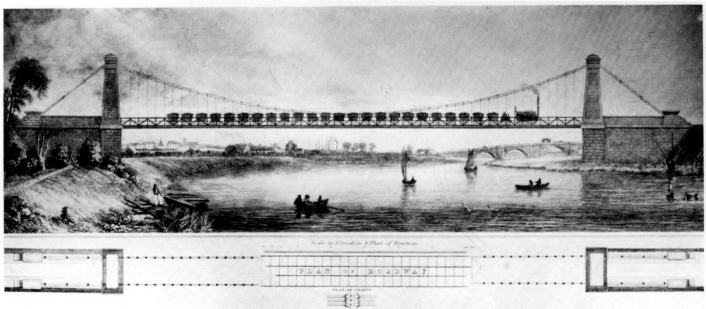

The boom of the iron industry in the 1850s followed the discovery of extensive ironstone deposits in the Cleveland Hills was led by Henry Bolckow and John Vaughan and saw the establishment of ironworks along the banks of the Tees by ironmasters including Bell Brothers, John Gjers and Sir Bernhard Samuelson.

The first works of Bolckow Vaughan (Teesside Archives)

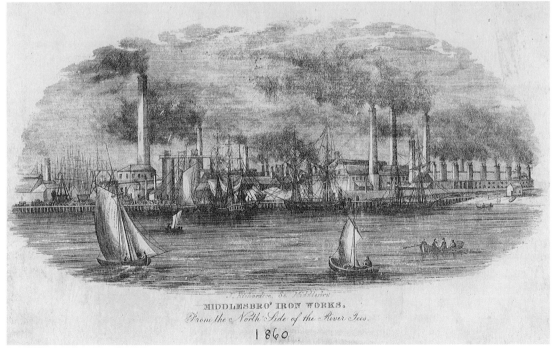

The 'Ironopolis' viewed from the north side of the River Tees, 1860 (Middlesbrough Libraries)

This industrial expansion and associated rapid urbanisation led to significant changes to the Teesside skyline as a once rural area was transformed into one dominated by furnaces and foundries along the Tees. Between the site of today's Transporter Bridge and Newport Bridge, the Ironmasters' District sprung up along the south bank of the Tees. These rapid developments led to heightened calls for new river crossings and the development of numerous proposals to bridge the Tees at Middlesbrough followed.

The Newport area in 1863 (Teesside Archives)

The ironworks at Newport in 1889 dominating the skyline (Teesside Archives)

The matter was complicated by the busy industrial river that meant any structure could not impede river traffic with piers in the water, whilst also accounting for the need to accommodate high-mast shipping. A number of innovative suggestions for solving the problem of the Tees followed in the ensuing decades.

On the Tees Middlesbrough.

In 1871, the North Eastern Railway Company sought to build a swing bridge over the river opposite Newport, on the Yorkshire side, and about 700 yards from where Billingham Beck enters the river on the Durham side. However, the proposals were met with opposition from local corporations and industrialists and the scheme failed to progress. The following year suggestions were made for a lift bridge – a railway crossing - at Newport by T.E. Laing but the scheme never progressed beyond the concept stage despite enthusiasm in the engineering community.

High-mast shipping on the Tees necessitated unconventional approaches to spanning the river (Dorman Museum)

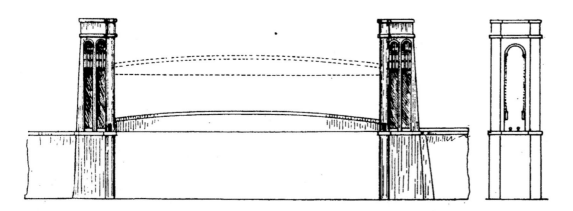

In 1873, a scheme to construct a transporter bridge or 'bridge ferry' across the Tees between Port Clarence and the town dubbed 'Ironopolis' was proposed by Charles Smith, Manager of the Hartlepool Ironworks. The costs associated with this novel method of transportation meant that the scheme failed to progress and instead investment was made in a cheaper horse and cart ferry scheme. In the same decade proposals for a tunnel under the Tees were met with objections from local officials and river authorities.

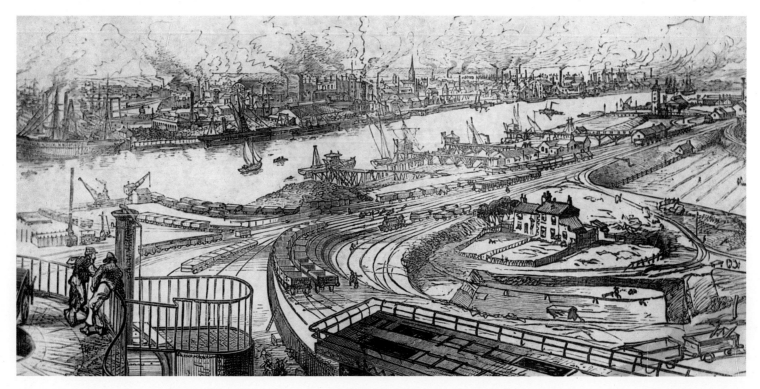

Later in the century, another proposed new bridge scheme across the Tees was discussed in the local press as the need for horse-drawn transport to cross the river were discussed. The proposed high-level bridge would have required significant approach roads at Port Clarence and St. Hilda's in order to gain sufficient height to facilitate continued high-mast shipping along the Tees and once more the proposals failed to progress.

PROPOSED NEW BRIDGE ACROSS THE TEES, AT MIDDLESBROUGH.

An 1890s sketch of a proposed new high-level bridge across the Tees at Middlesbrough (Middlesbrough Libraries)

Thus, until the early twentieth century the main means of crossing the river at Middlesbrough was by two main ferry routes - the Newport Ferry and the Middlesbrough-Port Clarence ferries. According to William Lillie's *History of Middlesbrough*, the Newport Ferry was first mentioned in the twelfth century. By the 1860s a keen commercial interest was taken in ferrying passengers between Newport and Stockton and the route was served by two competing firms – Dixon's and Duncan Brothers – who ran fantastically named ferries such as 'Catherine', 'Little Western', 'Royal Charlie', 'River King' and 'River Queen'.

A steamer at the bend of the Tees at Newport (British Steel Collection, Teesside Archives)

As demand increased new waiting rooms and improved infrastructure was put in place as the firms vied for supremacy. By the 1880s new ferries such as the 'Hornet' and 'Teaser' were introduced that improved crossings and into the twentieth century the 'Lady Magdalen' helped transport Teessiders across their river. The Newport ferry service was formally discontinued in 1934 with the opening of the Newport Bridge.

FERRY TIME TABLE.

Middlesbrough to Port Clarence

WEEK-DAYS.

a.m.	a.m.	a.m.	p.m.	p.m.	p.m.
5·15	8·30	11·45	2·30	5·30	8·30
5·30	8·45	12·0—Train	2·45	5·45	8·50—Train
5·45	9·0	p.m.	3·0	6·0	9·0
6·0	9·10—Train	12·15	3·15	6·15	9·15
6·15	9·30	12·30	3·30	6·30	9·30
6·30	9·45	12·45	3·45	6·45	9·45
6·45	10·0	12·55—Train	4·0	6·55—Train	10·0
6·55—Train	10·15	1·15	4·15—Train	7·15	10·15
7·15	10·30—Train	1·30	4·30	7·30	10·30
7·30	10·45	1·45	4·45—Train	7·45	10·45
7·45	11·0	2·0	5·0	8·0—Train*	11·0
7·55—Train	11·15	2·20—Train	5·15—Train	8·15	11·30
8·15	11·30			*Saturdays only.	12·0

The Boat returns from Port Clarence about Five Minutes after the times stated above.

On SUNDAYS the Boat plies every half-hour until 11 p.m., excepting when the time is varied as follows to suit the departure of Trains :—

8·0 a.m. and 5·40 p.m. for Billingham.

9·0 a.m. and 6·50 and 8·35 p.m. for Hartlepool.

SCALE OF CHARGES:

For every Passenger	...	...	1d
„ Horse, Mule, or Ass, and Rider or Driver			2d
„ Calf or Swine	...	...	1d
„ Ox, Cow, &c.	...	...	2d
„ Sheep or Goat	...	...	½d
„ Carriage, Wagon, &c., in addition to the Charge for Horses or other Animals drawing the same ... ... Not exceeding 10 cwt. 2d			

Not exceeding 1 ton		4d
Every additional 10 cwt.		2d
For every Hand-Cart, Barrow, Cycle, &c.	...	1d
For Goods not in any Conveyance. Not exceeding 14 lbs.		1d
„ 56 lbs.		3d
„ 5 cwt.		4d
„ 1 ton		6d

Every Passenger in any Conveyance, and every Driver of Cattle, Sheep, Swine, &c., and every Ox, Cow, Calf, Sheep, Swine, &c., in any Conveyance, to be charged for in addition to the charge on such Conveyance.

JOHN GETTINS,
SUPERINTENDENT.

JORDISON & Co., Ld., Printers and Lithographers, Middlesbrough.

Bridging the 'Steel River' in the twentieth century

In the early twentieth century, the haphazard ferry journeys across the Tees between Middlesbrough and Port Clarence were replaced with a 'flying ferry' or 'bridge ferry' suspended from the Transporter Bridge's main boon.

Opened by Prince Arthur, Duke of Connaught on 17th October 1911, the new Transporter Bridge was an innovative, ingenious, and sometimes irksome method of spanning the river. It removed the need for the often-perilous journey faced by the packed Erimus and Hugh Bell ferries across the river that would involve negotiating the tidal waterway and timely negotiation of the busy shipping that was transporting iron, steel and various other products to and from Middlesbrough and Port Clarence.

An extract from the Middlesbrough to Port Clarence Ferry Time Table (Teesside Archives)

With a moving car or gondola at road level suspended by cables from a track some 160ft above the Tees on the underside of a cantilever structure with an absolute height of 225ft, the suspended platform meant no obstructive piers in the water were necessary and thus large, high-mast vessels could continue to navigate the river. Moreover, those employed at the works on each bank of the Tees – there were dozens of firms in operation at Middlesbrough and Port Clarence during this period - could now be transported without encountering the terrors of the Tees.

In two minutes the workers could traverse the Tees and be on their way to or from work. In the coming years millions of passengers each year took advantage of this revolutionary crossing of the river. In 1922, some 3.7 million passengers were ferried between Middlesbrough and Port Clarence and by 1930 the number had increased to 5.3 million. Yet, like the ferries it was built to replace, the 'flying ferry' was often dangerously overcrowded to such an extent police intervention was required to restore order. Capacity and staffing proved challenging and in the summer months the Transporter Bridge staff had to work overtime to run extra trips to get those seeking a 'breath of briny' at Seaton Carew back home after a day out on the coast.

The Erimus was one of the main ways of crossing the Tees before the Transporter Bridge opening (Middlesbrough Libraries)

Inset: The Hugh Bell transports workers between Middlesbrough and Port Clarence (Teesside Archives)

A 1913 Tees Conservancy Commissioners depiction of the busy river (Teesside Archives)

In two minutes the workers could traverse the Tees and be on their way to or from work. In the coming years millions of passengers each year took advantage of this revolutionary crossing of the river. In 1922, some 3.7 million passengers were ferried between Middlesbrough and Port Clarence and by 1930 the number had increased to 5.3 million. Yet, like the ferries it was built to replace, the 'flying ferry' was often dangerously overcrowded to such an extent police intervention was required to restore order. Capacity and staffing proved challenging and in the summer months the Transporter Bridge staff had to work overtime to run extra trips to get those seeking a 'breath of briny' at Seaton Carew back home after a day out on the coast.

A packed Transporter Bridge gondola (Teesside Archives)

The Transporter Bridge transformed crossing the Tees between Middlesbrough and Port Clarence (Dorman Museum)

The rise of the motor vehicle too contributed to complicating crossing the Tees at Middlesbrough owing to the gondola's limited footprint with capacity for around 600 passengers, little room for even smaller vehicles and an inability to carry heavy vehicles. In fact, the Cleveland Bridge-designed landmark was closed to vehicular traffic at peak times as it struggled to cope with demand. The alternative crossing of the river was via Victoria Bridge linking Stockton and Thornaby which meant a round trip of eight miles compared to a crossing of less than two minutes. Such inadequate transport links led to costly delays for industrial transport, proved detrimental for commercial and leisure crossings of the Tees and added to calls for a new bridge.

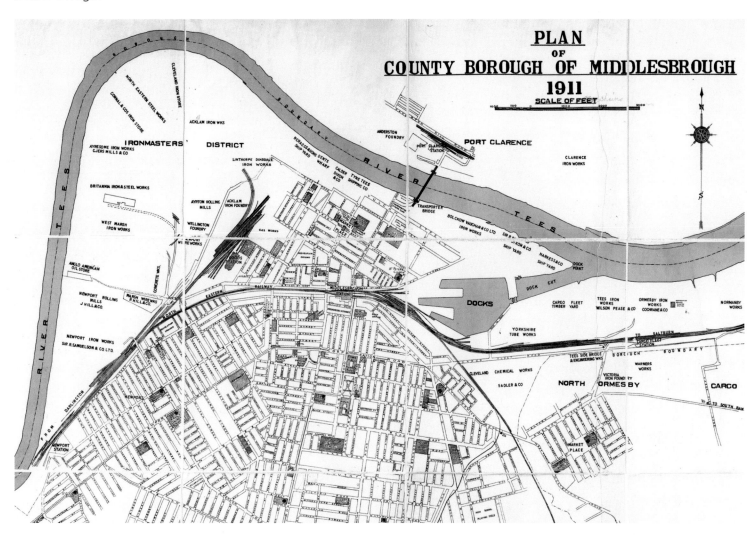

A plan of Middlesbrough 1911 (Middlesbrough Libraries)

Interwar Difficulties and Delays

"Again and again meetings...were held and the proposal for an additional crossing of the Tees discussed and argued. For a period of four years the Committees considered and reconsidered the nature of the crossing...the most appropriate site, and various reports of experts."

Tees Newport Bridge: Official Souvenir Programme, 1934

Significant economic difficulties experienced on Teesside during much of the 1920s heightened calls for a new crossing of the River Tees at Middlesbrough. A new bridge was considered a key mechanism for supporting access to new jobs and developing infrastructure that could support industrial recovery and expansion.

SIR BERNARD SAMUELSONS NEWPORT WORKS

An aerial view of Newport Ironworks in the early twentieth century (British Steel Collection, Teesside Archives)

The challenging twenties

Despite initial boom in the years immediately after the end of the First World War, contraction in demand for steel heralded the onset of economic strife. The recovery of Western European suppliers and unfavourable exchange rates contributed to a decline in the export of steel from Britain to the continent, whilst imports of iron and steel increased as British firms still recovered from the effects of war. These adverse conditions characterised the 1920s as Britain's place in the international market changed forever and Middlesbrough and surrounding towns endured a severe period of depression with blast furnaces out of blast and collieries, iron and steel plants stood idle.

Newport Ironworks was amongst the industries that had idle plant during the difficulties (Paul Stephenson)

In 1926 there was widespread economic chaos as industrial relations broke down with severe implications for manufacturing as production was brought to a halt. Whilst the coal stoppage brought by the General Strike was the standout industrial action, at Middlesbrough there was unrest including a strike at Middlesbrough Dock and tugboat troubles as tug crews refused to work following cutbacks by tug owners during the national strike.

An early twentieth century view of Middlesbrough Dock (Middlesbrough Libraries)

The worldwide economic crash of 1929 had a profound impact on local industry that had already endured years of turmoil and brought severe economic hardship for tens of thousands of Teessiders. The already ailing Bolckow Vaughan – the firm established by Middlesbrough's first ironmasters Henry Bolckow and John Vaughan - brought amalgamation with major steel manufacturers Dorman Long. The amalgamation meant that in the space of three decades Bolckow Vaughan had went from having been 'the biggest British iron producer and possibly the biggest steel producer in the world by 1900' to going out of existence having yielded to a sale forced through by the bank.

HENRY WILLIAM FERDINAND BOLCKOW
FOUNDER OF THE FIRM

JOHN VAUGHAN
FOUNDER OF THE FIRM

The end of the 1920s brought an end to Bolckow Vaughan, the firm founded by Henry Bolckow and John Vaughan (Teesside Archives)

The profound impact of economic difficulties on day-to-day life on Teesside is revealed in Kate Nicholas' excellent study *The Social Effects of Unemployment in Teesside, 1919-39* which details extreme levels of poverty, hunger, and economic-driven breakdown of relationships. Such severe social effects are hardly surprising when one considers that from 1920 until the opening of the Tees Newport Bridge in 1934 registered unemployed in Middlesbrough reached as high as 45 percent and dropped no lower than 15 percent. Thus, it became increasingly apparent to industrialists and local leaders that it was of crucial importance to open up new employment opportunities for the area.

CLOUDS OF DEPRESSION.— A scene in Middlesbrough Docks yesterday with empty berths and silent new cranes. Even the clouds seem to denote depression.

Clouds of depression at Middlesbrough Dock in the 1930s (Middlesbrough Libraries)

Improved transport was one major intervention that could stimulate economic growth by improving the logistical operations of existing firms and helping to attract new investment through improved infrastructure. This included ensuring the commercial needs of the long-established iron and steel industries were catered for and the new job opportunities maximised at Synthetic Ammonia and Nitrates (later ICI) on the north side of the river, described as amongst the 'most progressive works in the world...that was expected to engage, eventually, 10,000 employees'.

A new crossing would improve transport links for those already engaged in work on the other side of the Tees from their home, help support those seeking employment and open up opportunities through the rise of consumer society and new retail opportunities. Afterall, a new span across the Tees would also make it much easier to attract new customers from the other side of the river to the plethora of pubs, shops and restaurants to be found in Middlesbrough and Stockton-on-Tees town centres.

Long-running debates over a new crossing of the Tees

The idea of a new link across the Tees formally emerged just nine years after the opening of the Transporter Bridge when in 1920 a conference was called on the preparation of future Town Planning Schemes in connection with the Teesside area's industrial development. A suggestion to form Joint Committees made up of local authority representatives on the relative sides of the River Tees would help address the question of improving local transport infrastructure.

Preston Kitchen, Middlesbrough Town Clerk (Teesside Archives)

At a meeting of the Middlesbrough General Purposes Committee in November 1920 reported in the *Hartlepool Northern Daily Mail*, Town Clerk Preston Kitchen intimated that there was widespread recognition amongst civic leaders of the need for a new road between Middlesbrough and Redcar, whilst Alderman Joseph Calvert referred to 'the insufficient means of communication between North Yorkshire and Durham' and asserted that 'there ought to be through traffic from North Yorkshire to Durham which could be accomplished by a bridge across the river at Middlesbrough'. Notably, Calvert was not so certain as to who should take responsibility for such an undertaking, stating that he did not think it was for the local authority in Middlesbrough to construct the bridge!

The ensuing years would bring successive meetings of authorities and key stakeholders from the County of Durham and the North Riding of Yorkshire that were characterised by conflicting views on cost, location and even the method of any new cross-river link. Despite the overwhelming bulk of the evidence confirming the need for a bridge and the advice of experts having identified the best possible location for the crossing was that near Newport, the local authorities failed to unite behind a single way forward. Eston Urban District Council, serving an area to the east of Middlesbrough, expressed its preference for a link easterly not only of the proposed Newport site but also of the Tees Transporter Bridge. Meanwhile, representatives of Redcar Urban District Council - an area of growing industrial importance owing to the gradual shift of iron and steel production down river - considered Newport 'too far removed' from the coastal town. There was also the issue of continued access upriver beyond Middlesbrough that meant any crossing would have to provide enough clearance for shipping and not have prohibitive supports in the river or as a costly tunnel scheme.

A new bridge at Newport

Severe trade slump and question marks over who should fund the development and delivery of a new crossing eventually prompted local authorities to appeal to central government for support towards the project. It was not until 30th September 1924 that Newport site was finally selected as the location for a new link, despite the continued objections by those from authorities to the east unhappy at the westerly proposed location. The site received five votes for to two against (with two bodies remaining neutral). In close proximity to Dorman Long's Newport Ironworks – now home to Teesside Advanced Manufacturing Park (TeesAMP) – the location was closely embedded amongst established industry and well-placed for the anticipated large developments at Synthetic Ammonia and Nitrates.

An interwar plan of Newport Ironworks (British Steel Collection, Teesside Archives)

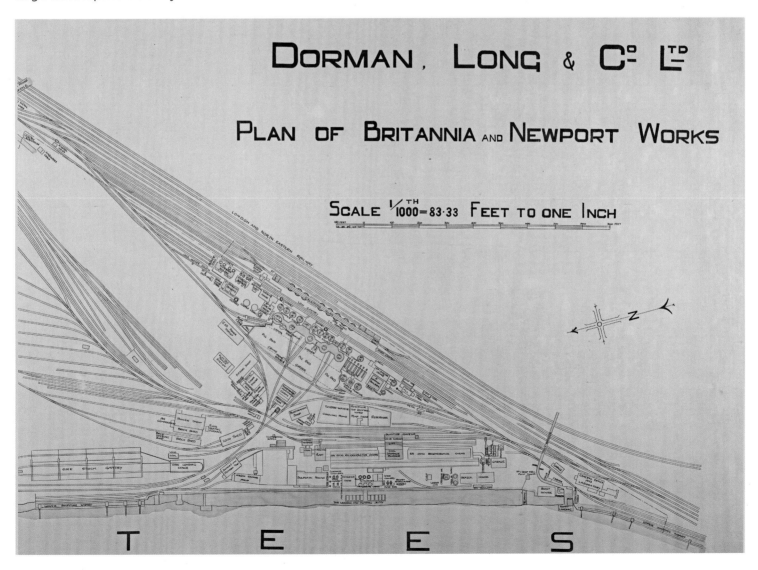

It was a letter sent by Durham County Council to Middlesbrough Corporation in December 1924 that prompted the next significant development as Middlesbrough and Durham joined together to partly fund the cost of plans and estimates for a crossing, with the Ministry of Transport contributing 50% of the cost.

Despite agreement on a location, further complications soon arose about the type of bridge that was to be adopted, prompting the *North Eastern Daily Gazette* to hit out at the lack of progress in an article dated 4th February 1926:

> Over a year has passed since the average Tees-sider told himself (after reading through the exhaustive, and exhausting, reports of various planning conferences on the subject) that there definitely was to be erected a new and revolutionising bridge across the river...That was over a year ago. This week the Tees Conservancy Commission agreed to consider the plans for the bridge – when they were submitted by the local authorities. Not very thrilling is it? At the present rate of progress it would appear that the Tees Crossing... is fast approaching the intermediate preamble stage. There's still hope for the generation after next.

Despite a 'Report on the proposed Tees Bridge' by the esteemed bridge engineers Mott, Hay and Anderson making a strong case for the adoption of a 'Vertical Lift Type...the most suitable for the large span and the heavy loads to be carried', ideas for a more costly tunnel began to gain support. By 1928 frustrations over the delays led Miss Ellen Wilkinson, Labour MP for Middlesbrough East, to ask the Minister of Transport

> Whether he had received any report with regard to a new crossing of the River Tees by bridge or tunnel from Middlesbrough to the north bank [and] whether he was aware that there is great congestion across the present Transporter; and whether, in view of the importance to Middlesbrough of the new industries on the north bank of the Tees, he will cause some inquiry to be made which will facilitate progress in the matter?

It will come as no surprise that consistent with the lack of advancement, the Minister of Transport considered the Teesside authorities 'capable of investigating the needs of their area without my holding an inquiry'. Another year ended without any sign of a bridge as negotiations with the firms and authorities impacted by the proposed bridge rumbled on. The local press ran headlines such as 'Five Years of Talk' and 'Costly Delay' and detailed continued talk of a tunnel that one expert declared would 'be a mile long and motorists would not use it'.

Extract from "North Eastern Daily Gazette," 15th March, 1929.

Slowly and laboriously the negotiations preliminary to the construction of a bridge across the Tees pursue their way. It is a pity that some means cannot be found of speeding things up. The need for a new means of crossing the river is urgent. At the present rate of progress the situation will be desperate long before the bridge is built. Everybody understands, of course, that where there are so many interests involved it is difficult to get anything done in a hurry, but this does seem to be a case where somebody might try to follow the well-worn admonition to " cut the cackle and come to the 'osses." The public need should be made the first consideration and no obstacles should be allowed to stand in the way of remedying the present state of affairs.

Progress at last

In April 1929 there were at last promising signs of progress with the all-important issue of funding addressed when the Ministry of Transport indicated that 75 percent of the costs for building the new bridge would be met by central government. Following a General Election that brought a hung parliament and a Labour minority government, in August 1929 the Ministry of Transport confirmed their willingness to contribute 75 percent towards the approved cost. Recognising the need to capitalise on this offer, the 'Tees (Newport) Bridge Bill' was deposited in Parliament, with objections raised through seven petitions against the Bill. The South Durham Steel and Iron Company and Dorman Long expressed concern at the disruption caused to their industrial activities both by the construction and subsequent use of the bridge. Dorman Long, whose Newport Ironworks ran alongside the site of the proposed structure, expressed concern at the disruption to 'traffic by rail, river and road to and from the said works'. The concerns of the South Durham Iron and Steel Company centred upon the consequences of the new approach roads which they argued would divide their land and hinder planned future developments that had been on-hold due to trade depression.

The technology of the vertical-lift design was also called into question in the various petitions, including from South Durham Steel and Iron Company who contested that the Bridge could be a 'very serious impediment to the navigation of the river and thus cause considerable injury to your Petitioners' business...if any defect should occur in the machinery or equipment for raising the vertical lifting span'. The local authority at Stockton-on-Tees expressed concern at the 'little or no experience in this country of a bridge with a vertical lifting span' and the potential traffic problems that might arise owing to delays in lifting the span.

An extract from the North Eastern Daily Gazette from 1929, published in the Tees Newport Bridge Opening Programme

> TRANSPORTER RUSH. As the Billingham Factory of the Imperial Chemical Industries extends its domain so does the number of employees who live on the South Bank of the Tees increase, and in proportion the congestion at the Tees Crossing becomes more and more acute. The trouble is that thousands of workers, all fired with a burning desire to get home quickly, combine in a simultaneous rush upon the Transporter Bridge. If this human torrent could be stemmed or released in moderation all would be well, but that seems an unattainable counsel of perfection.
>
> On a recent evening a horde of workmen released from 2 till 10 shift swarmed upon the transporter car; " and those behind urged those in front " with the result that a steel passenger doorway was forced off its rollers into the river, and a considerable delay ensued before it was rescued. All this, of course, emphasises the need for a bridge or tunnel.

An extract from the local press referencing the pressure on the Transporter Bridge brought by the new ICI works, republished in the Opening Programme

A slight degree of parochial self-preservation can be detected in other grievances raised. For instance, Stockton-on-Tees Corporation worried that the new link could hinder the 'new industries which will provide work for the population of your Petitioners' Borough'. Whether this simply reflected anxieties brought by trade slump and the closure of shipyards and Blairs Engineering Company's struggles that would eventually see the firm close in 1933, or reflected worries that jobs would be taken by people from south of the river is unclear. Elsewhere, the Tees Conservancy Commission's petition had underlying tones of objection to the erosion of their power, expressing concern that the passing of the Bill would allow 'works to be placed in the river or on the banks or foreshores...under your Petitioners' jurisdiction without your Petitioners' sanction'.

Resolving the petitions

Six of the seven petitions were addressed by means of agreement and protective clauses, leaving only Stockton Corporation in absolute objection. The ensuing Select Committee on Private Bills held in April 1930 was dubbed a 'Lively Duel' by the *North Eastern Daily Gazette* as recriminations of self-interest from the Stockton camp were made by Middlesbrough General Purposes Committee Chairman Colonel Thomas Gibson Poole. When Stockton's representative raised the issue of a tunnel as an alternative to a bridge, the former Mayor of Middlesbrough and member of the Tees Conservancy Commission and Ferry Committee retorted that such a scheme would cost £3,500,000 to £4,000,000. Gibson Poole was similarly dismissive of Stockton's suggestions that the proposed structure 'will be a danger to navigation going up to Stockton' by hitting back – in reference to the back and forth that had characterised almost a decade of discussions - that 'this kind of tosh was put up before'.

TEES (NEWPORT) BRIDGE BILL.

PETITION

PRAYING TO BE HEARD BY COUNSEL

AGAINST

To the HONOURABLE the COMMONS of the UNITED KINGDOM of GREAT BRITAIN and NORTHERN IRELAND in Parliament assembled.

The Humble Petition of Dorman Long and Company Limited under their Common Seal.

SHEWETH AS FOLLOWS:—

1. A Bill (hereinafter referred to as "the Bill") has been introduced and is now pending in your Honourable House entitled "A Bill to empower the Mayor Aldermen and Burgesses of the "County Borough of Middlesbrough and the County Council of "the Administrative County of Durham to construct a new bridge "over the River Tees and to execute other works in connection "therewith to provide for the vesting of the said bridge and "approaches; and for other purposes."

2. The Bill is promoted by the Mayor Aldermen and Burgesses of the county borough of Middlesbrough (in the Bill and hereinafter referred to as "the Corporation") and the county council of the administrative county of Durham (in the Bill and hereinafter referred to as "the County Council") and which Corporation and County Council are in the Bill and hereinafter referred to as the "two authorities." The Preamble of the Bill recites (*inter alia*) that the construction of a bridge across the River Tees for vehicular and pedestrian traffic with approaches thereto and with a vertical lifting span for the passage of vessels navigating that river would be of public and local advantage, and that the Minister of Transport has agreed to contribute three-quarters of the cost of constructing such a bridge and approaches and that it is expedient that the construction

Dorman Long's petition against the Tees (Newport) Bridge Bill, 1929-1930 (Teesside Archives)

The following day the Bill was approved to the delight of the promoters and a local press that had long expressed criticism at the 'tedious and torturous path of circles' that threatened the 'real needs of the community'. The Tees (Newport) Bridge Act received Royal Assent on 4th June 1930 and a new crossing of the Tees was on the way.

FIGHT FOR TEES BRIDGE

COLONEL POOLE'S VIEW OF OPPOSITION

N.E.D.G. ———————— 10.4.30.

MERELY "TOSH"

LIVELY DUEL WITH COUNSEL ON COURTESY

WESTMINSTER, Thursday.
COLONEL T. GIBSON POOLE, chairman of the General Purposes Committee of the Middlesbrough Corporation, was cross-examined by Mr Arthur Moon, K.C., representing the Stockton Corporation, when the Bill promoted by the Middlesbrough Corporation and Durham County Council for authority to construct a new bridge over the River Tees was further considered by a Select Committee of the House of Commons, Mr W. Wellock presiding.

The proposed bridge would cross the Tees at Newport and would connect with the Newport road on the south side and the Haverton Hill road on the north.

It is estimated to cost £616,000, and will be of a type new to this country, having a centre span between two piers 250 feet long, which will be raised bodily to a height of 120 feet to permit of the passage of shipping. It has been described as "a gigantic lift, and will have the largest opening span of any bridge in the country."

The only opposition appearing before

COLONEL T. G. POOLE.

The debates at Westminster received detailed coverage in the local press (North Eastern Daily Gazette, 10th April 1930)

THE NEW TEES BRIDGE TOO HIGH

EXPERT SUGGESTS PLANS SHOULD BE REVISED

TYNE AND WEAR EXAMPLES

EXCESSIVE PRECAUTIONS FOR UP RIVER TRAFFIC

A STATE promise of 75 per cent. of the cost makes the erection of the new Tees bridge virtually certain.

A prominent local technician—who prefers to remain anonymous—suggests, however, that unnecessary expense is being incurred by the excessive height of the proposed structure.

If the Tyne and Wear are spanned by bridges 82 and 83 feet, respectively, above high water level, what need, he asks, has the Tees for a bridge 160 feet above the high water mark.

UNNECESSARY EXPENDITURE

Numerous debates - including the argument the bridge was too high - featured in the press (North Eastern Daily Gazette)

Building the Bridge

"It is a bridge now, and such it will always be, for the two cross-girders will remain in position until the central span is completed."

The Northern Echo, 26th January 1933

With local disputes, parliamentary debates and legislative wrangling now largely resolved, progress on the scheme was more tangible. A Joint Committee was appointed to exercise the powers of the Act and met for the first time on 31st October 1930 with Middlesbrough's Alderman Gibson-Poole appointed Chairman and Durham County Council Councillor Peter Lee Vice-Chairman.

Dorman Long's joy

The question of who would build the bridge was resolved by the end of the year when the Joint Committee met to consider the tenders submitted. As might be expected, a number of the area's famed bridge builders and construction firms were among the thirteen tenders submitted. Local firms Cleveland Bridge & Engineering, Dorman Long, Furness Shipbuilding, Head Wrightson and Tees-side Bridge & Engineering competed alongside firms responsible for acclaimed bridges around the world including Sir William Arrol & Co. who had constructed the majestic Forth Bridge and the Tees Transporter Bridge.

Dorman Long, established in Middlesbrough in 1875 and by the late 1920s led by Sir Arthur Dorman and Sir Hugh Bell, were one of the largest steel manufacturers in the world. The local firm submitted the lowest tender at £436,913 11s 3d - by comparison, the highest priced tender submitted by The Horseley Bridge & Engineering Co. came in at £516,141 17s and the second-lowest tender came in at over £22,000 more than the Middlesbrough firm's bid. Ultimately, Dorman Long's bid was successful and added to the firm's ever-increasing portfolio of bridge contracts. The firm had completed the construction of the Tyne Bridge in 1928 and were busy building the monumental Sydney Harbour Bridge in Australia.

Sir Arthur Dorman, Chairman of Dorman Long, died in 1931 before Newport Bridge was completed (Middlesbrough Libraries)

Sir Hugh Bell, after whom one of the steam ferries across the Tees was named, was director and briefly chairman of Dorman Long (Middlesbrough Libraries)

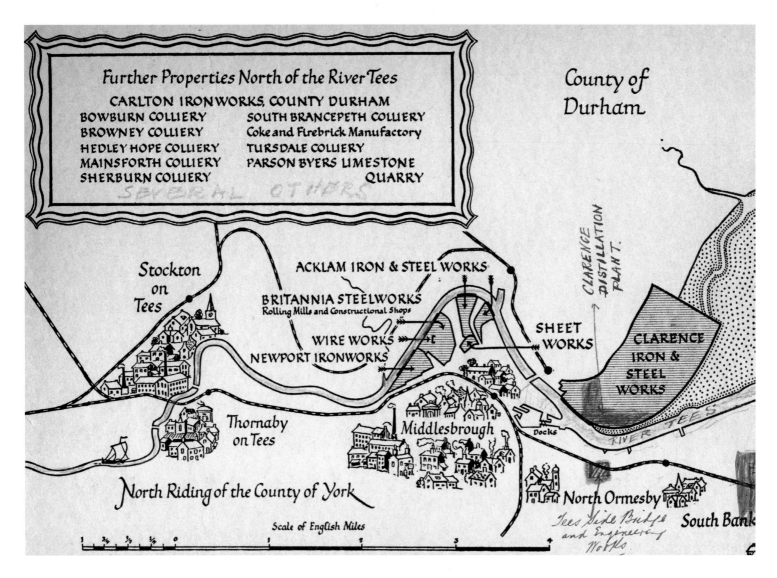

Back on Teesside, the award of the contract provided a shot in the arm for the local steel industry and, according to the opening brochure for the Tees crossing, was much welcomed in the area:

> Intense pleasure was occasioned to the Joint Committee and to Tees-side generally that the contract had been secured by a local firm, thus ensuring that practically the entire work would be executed by local labour and that the district which has suffered during many years seriously from unemployment would benefit to the greatest possible extent.

An extract from a Dorman Long British Empire Exhibition publication showing the extensive works of Dorman Long along the Tees (British Steel Collection, Teesside Archives)

Making way for the new crossing

The new structure to the design of engineers Mott, Hay and Anderson was to be Teesside's equivalent to the Tyne Bridge and Sydney's new crossing by bringing a striking change to the local skyline whilst providing a crucial new addition to transport infrastructure.

On the Middlesbrough side of the new bridge the construction of new approach roads required the removal of existing infrastructure and housing. A scheme was undertaken at Whinney Banks for the erection of 58 houses to rehouse most of the 70 tenant families displaced by the demolitions that, according to *The Northern Echo* of January 1932, saw houses 'knocked down like ninepins' and left Calvert and Samuelson Streets 'a scene of desolation'. The landing stage of the Newport Ferry – the means by which to cross the river at Newport that was to be superseded by the state-of-the-art bridge – was also relocated in 1931 in one of many riverside changes resulting from the new crossing.

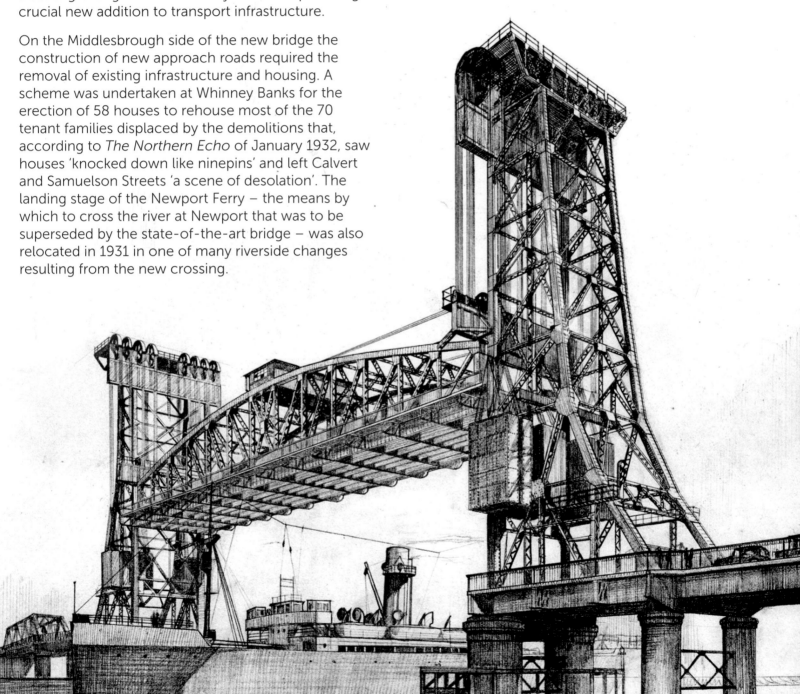

An artist impression of the proposed bridge over the Tees at Newport (Teesside Archives)

The focus of the early work by the contractor was on preparing the foundations and approaches to the new Bridge. Nevertheless, both the local press and national newspapers took great interest in the latest Tees landmark with regular photographic chronicling of different stages of construction works, which began in March 1931.

On 14th July 1932, the foundation stones were laid by Colonel Thomas Gibson Poole as Chairman of the Joint Bridge Committee in the shadow of the under-construction towers. However, it was not until late 1932 signs of the skyline-transforming steel structure were evident as the towers on each side of the Tees began to take shape.

Doomed – the local press reports on the demolition of streets in 1931 and 1932 (North Eastern Daily Gazette and The Northern Echo)

DEMOLISHING TWO STREETS.

Where Samuelson-street, Newport, Middlesbrough, once was. More Newport bridge pictures in the back page.

—[N.E.

N. ECHO   8/1/32.

HOUSES KNOCKED DOWN LIKE NINEPINS.

PREPARING FOR THE ROAD TO MIDDLESBRO'S NEW BRIDGE.

The first crossing

The Tees at Newport was first spanned on 25th January 1933 with the fixing of a 30-ton girder to the two towers in what *The Northern Echo* dubbed a visible sign of progress which 'had been absent from the more intricate processes which have been going on for some time on and in the towers'. The fixing of the girder as a false span was watched by hundreds of people lining the Tees with the process of lifting from the barge to the top of the Bridge some 160ft about the river taking little more than two hours. According to the newspaper report of the milestone, erector W. Canwell of North Ormesby was the source of the biggest thrill for onlookers:

> He [Canwell] had need to get an instruction over to the Durham side of the job. So he walked out on to the girder, which had an unprotected width of not more than 10 inches, crossed to the other side, remained there a few moments, and then returned. Every few yards he had to swing his foot over the joint of the interlacing, but he never slackened pace, and on reaching the Yorkshire side went nonchalantly on with his job.

Progress in completing the main lifting span was rapid, with *The Northern Echo* reporting how the affixing of the last member in May 1933 was marked by the hoisting of the Union flag on the Bridge. Sadly, whilst the structure took shape over the Tees, there was also tragedy above it in March 1933 when construction workers Jack Thompson and William McKittrick lost their lives and another narrowly escaped death after a ladder broke at the top of the Bridge. Tragically, the two men fell into the Tees and struck a barge that was transporting Dorman Long steelwork on the river. The other man, Harry Dorrington of Thornaby, fell from the top of the Bridge but managed to grab a projecting girder and was able to scramble to safety from what he later described as the 'most agonising moments in his life'. Sadly, they proved not to be the last deaths to occur on or around the crossing of the Tees with several people having lost their lives during the ensuing decades owing to road accidents and falls.

By October 1933, the question of who would officially open the Tees Bridge was the subject of press speculation, with some articles suggesting the Prince of Wales would return to the town less than four years on from opening Constantine College in 1930. However, with the Prince of Wales unavailable it was revealed in early December 1933 that the honour of performing the official opening in February 1934 would be bestowed on the Duke and Duchess of York.

Preparing for lift-off

In preparation for the opening of the new Tees landmark, a number of appointments were made to the Bridge staff. Mr J.A.K. Hamilton was appointed Resident Engineer on a salary of £700 a year, leading one councillor to hit out at what he considered an excessive salary given that the men who had built the Bridge were paid £4 a week. A series of tests were conducted, including the first lift reported in the press in December 1933. Three different means were used to operate the bridge – the main electrical machinery, the reserve petrol engine apparatus and hand power. The latter method consisted of three men working an ordinary hand pulley to raise and lower the Bridge! Engineer Mr Anderson, one of the partners in Mott, Hay and Anderson, described the occasion as a 'proud moment', dubbed the structure 'a perfect industrial tool' and paid tribute to builders Dorman Long.

A History of Tees (Newport) Bridge produced by Stockton-on-Tees Borough Council provides a useful overview of the apparatus and process:

> The principal machinery for raising and lowering the span is located at mid-span in a housing built off the top of the two main trusses. Twenty feet (6.1m) below is the control room from which the bridge is driven. The machinery is comprised, essentially of a 750 horse power AC motor driving a 545 kW DC generator and two 325 horse power DC motors which are connected through reduction gearing to four 6 ft 6 in (1.98m) diameter winding drums mounted in pairs directly above each truss. The span was moved by four sets of wire haulage ropes which are anchored to the tops and bottoms of the towers and pass either under or over deflector sheaves and along and above the top chord of each truss to the winding drums at mid-span. To raise the span, the winding drums were rotated and wound in the uphaul ropes and passed out the downhaul ropes, the process being reversed for lowering the span. The time taken to raise or lower the span its full 99 feet (30.2m) of travel was 1½ minutes. Flat bottomed rails are fixed to the vertical faces of the towers which fit into guides on the ends of the span to prevent the span from swinging out of position.

In January 1934, members of the Newport Bridge's Joint Committee paid a visit to the new structure where they enjoyed a crossing and visited the control house on top of the lifting span. All that was left to do now was to get ready for the Royal Visit on 28th February 1934. Arrangements were made for the Duke and Duchess of York to stay at Wynyard Hall on the night before the ceremony and testing continued on the lead up to the big day. This included lifting the 2,745 tons of steel that made up the 270ft long span in high winds and ensuring the road gates, traffic lights, semaphore and navigation lights were all in working order. In order to test the structure's ability to cope with the additional weight posed by snow, some 30 tons of cast iron blocks were placed on the span and tests repeated.

A week ahead of the grand opening, workers were busy finishing work on the roadway and a select party of visiting engineers and guests were afforded an informal inspection of the engineering marvel that straddled County Durham and Yorkshire. Two days prior to the official opening, thousands flocked to the Bridge as painters put the final touches of green paint to the structure as they battled high winds that were driving smoke in their direction from the nearby Newport Ironworks' coke ovens. The day before the official opening, final tests were carried out in gales estimated at blowing at 80 miles an hour as the Bridge proved its ability to operate in even the most challenging of conditions. The Tees' new crossing was now ready for Royalty.

Members and officials of the Joint Committee cross the lifting span for the first time (Middlesbrough Libraries)

DONE IN TWO MINUTES

Engineers See New Tees Bridge Lift Test

Further successful tests of the Tees (Newport) Bridge, Middlesbrough, were carried out yesterday in the presence of Mr David Anderson, of Mott, Hay and Anderson, Westminster, the consulting engineers; Mr J. Hamilton, resident engineer; Mr J. T. Prendergast, agent of Dorman, Long and Company, the contractors; and Mr P. Hallitt, the chief engineer to Messrs Broadbents, of Huddersfield, who have supplied the lifting machinery.

While the span was moving, it was impossible to detect any vibration, and the lift was accomplished within two minutes. There was a strong wind blowing at the time, and this made the test even more severe.

The bridge will be opened by the Duke of York on February 28.

The local press report on successful tests of the structure, 10th February 1934 (North Eastern Daily Gazette)

A view of the Tees from the bridge ahead of the official opening (North Eastern Daily Gazette)

Building a landmark: photographs from Teesside Archives

The collection of photographs that follow capture different stages of the construction process. The images were digitised from the collections of Teesside Archives and a selection displayed at the Heritage Gallery at Cargo Fleet in 2014 as part of 'The Green One and The Blue One' exhibition to celebrate the 80th anniversary of the Tees Newport Bridge.

5426.
19-4-1932.

The Tees 'Wonder Bridge' Opens

"The scene at the Bridge was a magnificent spectacle of colour. In the background towered the great structure of the Bridge awaiting the touch of the Royal hand to bring it to life."

The North Eastern Daily Gazette, 28th February 1934

The end of February 1934 brought a new beginning for Teesside as communication between the north and south banks of the Tees was transformed in a Royal showpiece occasion as the Duke and Duchess of York visited the district to perform the official opening ceremony of the Tees Newport Bridge. Having arrived at Wynyard Hall the previous night, the Duke of York paid a visit to ICI Billingham on the morning of 28th February, with his keen interest in the plant resulting in a delayed return to Wynyard Hall. From there he was joined by the Duchess of York as they embarked on their journey to the Ironopolis.

One area of contention around the arrangements for the ceremony was the lack of provision for the children of Middlesbrough to join in the festivities as the area celebrated their new bridge. There was no holiday for local school children and arrangements for thousands of senior children to assemble at Levick Crescent to greet the Duke and Duchess of York on their entry into the town were abandoned owing to the snowy conditions, with it considered too much of a risk taking some 7,000 children out on the streets. Despite the lack of formal arrangements, newspaper reports from the day and family stories passed down through generations reveal a considerable number of children managed to make it out of the classroom to line the route to the Tees. Artist Craig Hatton's mother – who went on to work for Dorman Long during the Second World War - was amongst the children let out of school to attend the ceremony, whilst Gaynor Duffy's mother was permitted by her mother to take a day off from Archibald School so that the seven-year-old did not miss the event!

Close to the new structure at the Middlesbrough approach, the great and the good were gathered at a temporary grandstand to greet the Royal party and the Durham Light Infantry lined the approach to the Bridge with the glare of national media attention on the event. As the Duchess and Duke of York approached there were cheers from the crowd before the Duchess was presented with a bouquet from Gibson Poole. The formalities then commenced with Town Clerk Preston Kitchen reading a loyal address, to which the Duke of York replied:

> It gives me great pleasure indeed to be here and to declare open this Tees (Newport) Bridge, the first of its kinds in this country and the largest of its

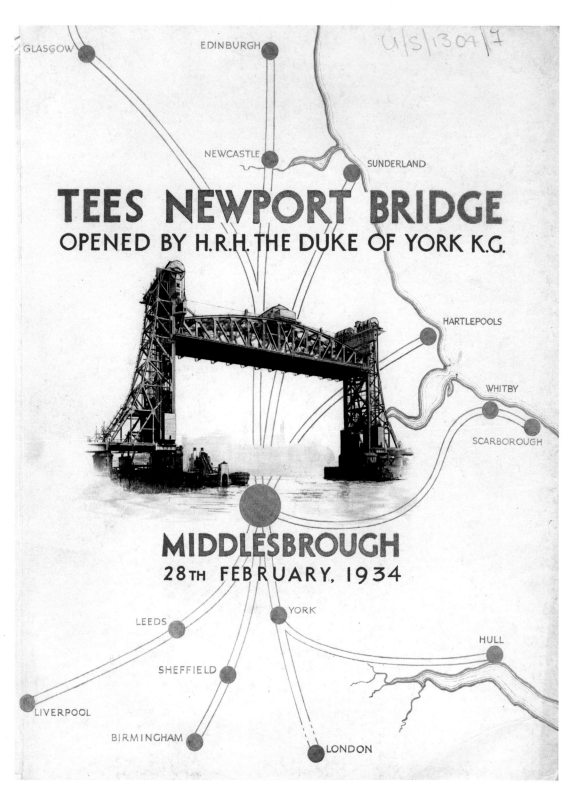

*Tees Newport Bridge
Opening Programme
(Teesside Archives)*

type in the world. In so doing I congratulate the engineers, Messrs. Mott, Hay and Anderson, and the contractors, Messrs. Dorman, Long and Company, Limited...I sincerely hope that this Bridge will be a complete and lasting success, and that it will fulfil all the high hopes that are held for it and prove to be of enduring service and benefit to the communities upon Tees-side, and indeed to the country at large.

The King's Speech

Film footage surviving from the event suggests the Duke of York – noted for a speech impediment that gained international attention through the movie *The King's Speech* – captures further parts of the address which the future King struggled to deliver with long pauses between words:

> The Duchess of York and I, thank you very sincerely for the loyal and cordial welcome which you have extended to us here today and we are very happy to have this opportunity of paying a visit to the Teesside district...Ladies and Gentlemen, I have much pleasure in declaring the Tees Newport Bridge open.

Following his address, the Duke of York then stepped forward to pull an electric switch that sounded warning sirens and lowered the span to road level. After the gates opened, the Royal party and dignitaries were unexpectedly joined by hundreds of gatecrashers who flooded forward to join them on the main span as they were elevated 120ft above the Tees. In fact, the police struggled to contain the throng of people and the last man to join the journey above the Tees had to do so by jumping onto the already lifting span!

The Royal pair took a keen interest in the workers on the Bridge, mechanisms for operation and the surrounding Teesside landmarks as the Acklam Cross passed beneath the structure to become the first vessel to pass under the newly opened bridge.

After the span was lowered, the Royal couple then proceeded to the Durham side where they inspected the first all-electrically welded bridge built in the country. Erected over the Billingham Branch line of the London and North Eastern Railway, the welded steel bridge was described in the day's souvenir programme as having a 'very clean and pleasing appearance' owing to the 'absence of all rivet-heads on the steelwork'.

ADDRESS TO BE PRESENTED TO H.R.H. THE DUKE OF YORK, K.G., P.C., K.T., G.C.M.G., G.C.V.O., AND H.R.H. THE DUCHESS OF YORK, G.B.E.

COUNTY PALATINE OF DURHAM
COUNTY BOROUGH OF MIDDLESBROUGH

TO

HIS ROYAL HIGHNESS THE DUKE OF YORK
AND
HER ROYAL HIGHNESS THE DUCHESS OF YORK

May it please Your Royal Highnesses,

We, the County Council of the Administrative County of Durham and the Mayor, Aldermen and Burgesses of the County Borough of Middlesbrough, jointly extend to Your Royal Highnesses a sincere and hearty welcome to Tees-side and to our respective County and County Borough, and beg you to accept our cordial and respectful thanks for so graciously consenting to appear amongst us.

We desire to take this opportunity of expressing our loyal devotion and allegiance to His Majesty the King. We would wish also to assure you that we share the affection and esteem in which Your Royal Highnesses and your beloved children are held, not only by the people of this Country, but throughout the British Empire.

We recall with pleasure the various occasions upon which Durham and Middlesbrough have been honoured by visits from Members of the Royal Family.

We have asked Your Royal Highnesses to come to Middlesbrough to declare open for traffic a new connecting link between the two great Counties of Yorkshire and Durham. This new Bridge, which we, assisted by the Ministry of Transport, have jointly built at a cost of £512,000 is in design new to this Country, and whilst many of a similar type have been built, chiefly in Canada and the United States of America, it is of its kind the largest in the world.

Extract of the address presented to the Duke and Duchess of York

SEEING TEESSIDE FROM 120 FEET UP.

HAPPY OPENING CEREMONY.

A Sunny Day and a Smiling Duchess.

"I AM DELIGHTED."

"**I** AM DELIGHTED with all that I have seen on my first visit to Middlesbrough," remarked the Duchess of York to the Mayor (Coun. Alfred Cooper) on bidding goodbye yesterday.

The Duke of York told the Mayor that he very keenly appreciated the warmth of the welcome given to the Duchess and himself. He had been keenly interested in all he had seen.

To the Chairman of the Tees (Newport) Joint Bridge Committee (Ald. T. Gibson Poole), the Duke expressed thanks for the extreme cordiality of the reception, and said that he would long remember the generous way in which he had been received and the kindliness of the townsfolk towards the Duchess.

After declaring open the new Tees Bridge the Duke and Duchess went up on the lifting span. From a height of 120 feet the Mayor of Middlesbrough pointed out to them various features of the Teesside landscape.

Then the Duchess walked up to one of the workmen and asked him about his job, and how the bridge mechanism worked.

It was the first visit of the Royal couple to Teesside since they were at Stockton for the Railway Centenary celebrations in 1925. On that occasion they created a most favourable impression. Yesterday they bound the hearts of the people of the area more firmly in affection towards the Royal Family.

The forebodings of bad weather created the previous day were dispelled as the sun gradually got the measure of all other atmospheric influences, giving the opening ceremony a completing touch of brightness which will make it an abiding memory.

The Duke and Duchess were met by the Chief Constable (Mr. Donald Heald) at the borough boundary at Acklam, and were escorted through Linthorpe, along Linthorpe-road and Newport-road to the bridge. From Cambridge-road the Duke and Duchess were received by continuous and cheering rows of spectators.

In spite of the cold morning the Royal visitors were in an open car (having changed the cars at Stockton), and their geniality pleased everyone.

Most of the people in the streets were women and girls. At the junction of Newport-road and Linthorpe-road women must have predominated over men to the extent of ten to one. The Duchess was constantly acknowledging their greetings.

OVERTIME AT BILLINGHAM.

Owing, it is understood, to the Duke's prolonged stay at the Billingham works of Imperial Chemical Industries, the procession was about 15 minutes late.

At the bridge approach the Mayor received the Duke and the Duchess. While the Duke inspected a company of the 1st Batt. Durham Light Infantry, under Major E. T. Heslop, the Duchess talked to the Mayor. In addition to the band and bugle section, under Bandmaster A. W. Woodham, 100 men of the battalion were on parade.

The Royal visitors then walked the 150 yards to the bridge in the company of the Mayor, the Lord Lieutenant of the North Riding (the Hon. Geoffrey Howard), the Lord Lieutenant of Durham (Lord Londonderry), Lord Castlereagh and others. Among those on the stands were representatives of

Seeing Teesside From 120 Feet Up - the local press report on the Royal Party's trip on the lifting span (The Northern Echo)

DUKE OF YORK OPENS NEW TEES BRIDGE

"I SINCERELY HOPE THAT THIS BRIDGE WILL BE A COMPLETE AND LASTING SUCCESS . . . ."
With these words the Duke of York yesterday opened the new Tees bridge at Newport, Middlesbrough, the first of its kind in the country and the largest of its type in the world. Above: The Duke pressing the button which lowered the 270-feet long span weighing 2,745 tons. Right: The Duchess of York and the Marquis of Londonderry watching the span descend to road level.—[N.E.]

The local press featured several pages of photographs of the opening ceremony (The Northern Echo)

THURSDAY, The Daily Mail MARCH 1, 1934

"GATE-CRASHERS" AT ROYAL BRIDGE-OPENING CEREMONY

DUCHESS'S HANDSHAKE FOR A WORKMAN

A DAY OF THRILLS AND SHIVERS

TOWN CLERK SAVES MOTOR-CAR FROM DISASTER

From CLIFFORD SPEIGHT
MIDDLESBROUGH, Wednesday.

WITH a wild nor'-easter whipping their faces to a rosy glow, tugging at coats and hats, and whistling round them, the Duke and Duchess of York were to-day carried aloft on the largest spanned bridge in the world at Newport, near here.

National newspaper headlines reported on the lifting span's gatecrashers (The Daily Mail)

Celebrations at Middlesbrough Town Hall and a gold toilet seat

Before the Duke and Duchess of York headed back to London there was time for a celebratory luncheon to mark the 'red letter day' in the history of the district. The Royal party made their way to Middlesbrough Town Hall for the celebration as thousands of Teessiders lined the route to catch a rare glimpse of the Royal couple. Bedecked with bunting and flags, the Town Hall was a scene of high pomp as the great and the good gathered to celebrate the new crossing. Retiring Rooms for the Royal dignitaries were laid out especially at the venue to accommodate the guests of honour, with an account by Cecil Parker, who worked on preparing the rooms, providing a fascinating look behind-the-scenes of the big day:

> I remember the opening of the Bridge; I was an apprentice in the Cabinet Shop at Dickson & Benson's and our company was given the job of preparing 'Retiring rooms' for the Royal visitors to use during the ceremony at the Town Hall after the Bridge Opening. The rooms were the offices at each side of the Town Hall entrance and both had a toilet adjoining...The rooms were stripped of all unnecessary fittings and Hill's the decorators came in and re-painted and papered the walls etc. Baker Bros fitted new plumbing and Dickson & Benson's carpeted and furnished them. There was an entrance door at the Albert Road end and another door to the toilet lobby, which enabled one to enter the right-hand room, walk through into the lobby, turn left, across the Town Hall entrance hall and do the reverse in the other room and down the Town Hall steps into Albert Road.

> We made and erected a handrail barrier across each room to create a walkway round the two rooms and then removed it – but ready to refix when the Royal party had left. The scheme was to allow the public in to view the rooms 'As used by their Royal Highnesses'...the G.P.O. had fitted a 'gold' telephone in the Duchess's room and Baker Bros had found a 'gold' seat for the toilet and the *Gazette* at the time had hyped this up in advance.

> When the time came for opening 'the show' the queue stretched along Albert Road and into Russell Street. I don't know how much was taken in entrance money, but it must have been acceptable.

The *North Eastern Daily Gazette* reported that more than 3,000 people – mostly women – filed through the two rooms on the day, each paying 2d for the privilege with money going to the Mayor's Boot and Shoe Fund. The temporary banqueting hall was also opened the following evening for the public to visit with proceeds supporting the same fund.

On leaving Middlesbrough, the Duchess told Mayor Councillor Alfred Cooper 'I am delighted in all that I have seen on my first visit to Middlesbrough' having spent part of the lunch bonding with Mayoress Cooper over their common Scottish ancestry.

The big day had been a success. The Tees Bridge was finally complete – excluding work still required on the Durham side link road - and ready to serve the people of Teesside. The *North Eastern Daily Gazette* front page from the day read 'The Tees Wonder Bridge Opens' and contended the new span provided Dorman Long with a 'standing advertisement of their skill...on their own doorstep'.

In total, the new Bridge and approaches boasted a total length of 4,920ft with 250ft clear width of river between the piers. The 270ft lifting span had a 120ft clearance above high water when fully raised and was capable of lifting in 90 seconds when electrically driven and in two minutes using the reserve petrol engine. Completed nineteenth months after the laying of the foundation stone – although construction began in March 1931 - the scheme cost a total of £512,352 and was the largest vertical-lift bridge of its type in the world. More importantly for Teessiders, the new lift bridge by Dorman Long lifted spirits by opening up major new economic opportunities for the district by enhancing connectivity to the new industrial opportunities on the Tees' north bank and the commercial and retail offer on the south bank of the river. The opportunity was certainly not lost on several Middlesbrough retailers who ran bridge-themed advertisements in the *North Eastern Daily Gazette* on the opening day that specifically targeted Billingham shoppers!

ROOMS THE DUKE AND DUCHESS USED.

VISITED BY 3,000 PEOPLE AT MIDDLESBROUGH.

More than 3,000 people yesterday afternoon and last night filed through the two specially furnished rooms at the Middlesbrough Town Hall which had been used by the Duke and Duchess of York earlier in the day.

A charge of 2d per person was made. The whole of the proceeds will go to the Mayor's Boot and Shoe Fund. The banqueting hall, as decorated and laid out for the Royal visit, will be open to the public to-night for the same cause.

The local press report on visits to the Royal Rooms in the Town Hall (The Northern Echo)

Mayor Alfred Cooper (Middlesbrough Libraries)

A diagram of the Tees (Newport) Bridge from the souvenir opening brochure, 1934

CO. DURHAM

TEES (NEWPORT) BRIDGE

Construction commenced March 1931
Opened to traffic 28th February 1934

MIDDLESBROUGH

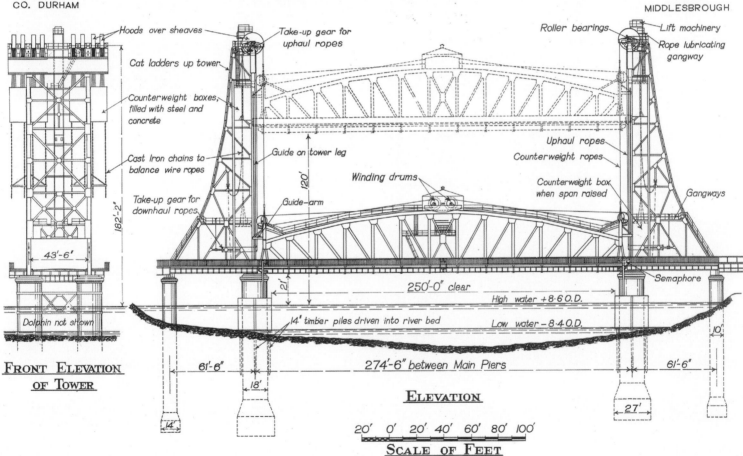

Hoods over sheaves

Cat ladders up tower

Counterweight boxes, filled with steel and concrete

Cast Iron chains to balance wire ropes

Take-up gear for downhaul ropes

Take-up gear for uphaul ropes

Guide on tower leg

Guide-arm

Winding drums

Roller bearings

Lift machinery

Rope lubricating gangway

Uphaul ropes

Counterweight ropes

Counterweight box when span raised

Gangways

Semaphore

182'-2"

120'

43'-6"

2'

250'-0" clear

High water +8·6 O.D.

14' timber piles driven into river bed

Low water −8·4 O.D.

Dolphin not shown

**FRONT ELEVATION
OF TOWER**

61'-6"

18'

14'

274'-6" between Main Piers

ELEVATION

27'

61'-6"

10'

20' 0' 20' 40' 60' 80' 100'

SCALE OF FEET

Snapshots of a 'red letter' day: photographs from Middlesbrough Reference Library

Digitised from a photograph album held in the collections of Middlesbrough Reference Library, the images that follow provide a unique snapshot of the opening ceremony and celebrations on 28th February 1934.

The Early Years

"Perfect satisfaction with the working of the new Tees (Newport) Bridge is expressed on Tees-side. Already a large volume of traffic has passed over the wonderful structure, and, as a much-needed means of communication, the crossing has immediately proved an immense boon."

North Eastern Daily Gazette, 8th March 1934

Just as the new bridge scheme had stirred up interest amongst engineers, local politicians, and the general public before and during construction, the largest bridge of its type in the world proved to be a big draw to a variety of groups and bodies over the years as a combination of commercial, concerns and curiosity created interest in the crossing.

A sketch from the Opening Programme showing the anticipated array of traffic to use the crossing (Teesside Archives)

Cinematic celebrations, commercial benefits and troublesome children

Two nights after the opening event a film of the opening ceremony was presented to Mayor Cooper during a civic visit to the town's Gaumont Palace where the Gaumont-British newsreel was shown to members of the Council, local officials and key figures associated with the bridge scheme.

As well as coverage on the big screen, the local press took a keen interest in the operations of the Bridge and chronicled early performance in their column inches. A week after opening, *The Northern Echo* reported that the Bridge had attracted thousands of sightseers, had an average of seven lifts a day and had brought economic and logistical benefits:

> Newport has awakened to a consciousness of extra importance. Shops and other business premises in the Newport district have already felt the benefit in increased takings...men engaged at the works of Imperial Chemical Industries at Billingham find it a boon. Many cycle; some even walk to and from work by means of the Bridge. In ten minutes, 220 cycles crossed.

The retail benefits are an interesting point given that just weeks before Newport Bridge opened Mr R.M. Cooper, President of the Stockton, Thornaby and District Grocers' and Provision Dealers' Association, predicted that the new link would be a 'white elephant'. At the meeting at Laing Café in Stockton, Councillor J.T. Johnson was similarly dismissive of any draw away from the shops of Stockton, stating that he 'saw no reason why Stockton should entertain any fears about Middlesbrough obtaining more trade to the detriment of the older borough with the opening of the new Bridge', stating 'people, after crossing the Bridge from the North side, would still be as near to Stockton as they would to the shopping centre of Middlesbrough'.

The Grand Opera House, later home to the Gaumont Palace (Paul Stephenson)

Binns were amongst the retailers keen to capitalise on the new bridge (Middlesbrough Libraries)

Beyond discussions of local communities looking elsewhere for their groceries, there were other concerns in the early days of operation. Young people posed a challenge owing to 'destructiveness of hordes of children' who had torn concrete pillars from their foundations at Newport Bridge and prompted calls for police to pay closer attention! Children playing on the structure also posed a danger to their own safety, including that of 12-year-old George Denney of Cannon Street who in July 1934 fell from one of the girders and suffered a suspected fractured jaw and general bruises. Two years later five-year-old Kenneth Dixon of Victoria Street received treatment at the North Riding Infirmary after falling 20ft from the structure whilst playing.

Despite some destructive children, groups of younger people with decidedly more positive intentions were drawn to the engineering masterpiece. The Middlesbrough Council of Boys Clubs and the Scientific Society of Constantine College were amongst the groups that paid a visit, whilst enquiries as to the workings of this curiosity of engineering were forthcoming from as nearby as Spennymoor to as far afield as Sydney, Australia.

Newport Road and Newport Hotel, Middlesbrough.

The new link helped better connect businesses and communities of Newport to the north bank of the Tees (Paul Stephenson)

Closer to home, *The Northern Eastern Daily Gazette* of the day spoke in glowing terms of a watercolour created by a local artist within two weeks of the new bridge opening:

> The new Tees Bridge, in addition to being an engineering triumph, has also an appeal for the artist. Mr T. Val Stephenson, a member of the staff of the Middlesbrough Education Offices, is believed to have the distinction of producing the first water-colour of the bridge.
>
> This painting, which is being exhibited in a window of Messrs Dickson and Benson's store, measures 26 ½ by 20 ½ inches, and depicts the structure from the Durham side, with the Newport Ironworks in the background. It is an evening study, and Mr Stephenson has captured the sky effects in subtle fashion. He made three visits to the site, and the painting was completed in a week.
>
> An old pupil of the Hugh Bell School, Mr Stephenson makes painting a hobby, and had drawing lessons at the evening classes at the High School and the Constantine College. About two years ago he exhibited a water-colour of the Transporter at the exhibition of the Cleveland Sketching Club.

Alongside the spectacle of the new crossing, there was also a period of brief alarm in the press in the month after opening following rumours that the structure was subsiding and that there was movement in the foundations. The Bridge Joint Committee officials moved quickly to address the stories and stressed that there was 'not the slightest truth' in the rumours.

REPLY TO A TEES BRIDGE RUMOUR.

"NO MOVEMENT IN FOUNDATIONS."

In March 1934 the Joint Bridge Committee denied reports that the structure was subsiding (The Northern Echo)

T. Val Stephenson's watercolour of the new crossing of the Tees, 1934 (Dorman Museum)

Counting the costs of the new crossing

The first-year performance of the Tees Bridge revealed that on an ordinary day some 1,728 motor vehicles, 4,224 cycles and 2,208 pedestrians used the crossing, whilst over the course of the year the lifting span was raised and lowered 1,500 times without any major delay. The electricity costs for operating the span and associated lighting and maintenance were approximated at £540 (equating to 5s 4½d per lift). However, there were some economic drawbacks felt elsewhere with Transporter Bridge takings dropping to less than £10,000 compared to over £15,000 five years earlier as the number of users dropped by 25 percent.

There was also the loss of £600 in receipts from the Billingham and Newport ferry that had previously ferried people across the Tees but had now ceased. Despite these losses, the *Daily Telegraph* Supplement *Teesside and its Industries* was full of praise for Middlesbrough's iconic crossings:

> Typical of the spirit of enterprise associated with all phases of Middlesbrough's life are the two remarkable bridges which link the town with the Durham side of the river. The Transporter Bridge, with its travelling platform, was opened in 1911, and is much the largest of its kind in the country.
>
> No less unusual is the Tees (Newport) Bridge, of the vertical lift type, opened in 1934, and the largest vertical lift bridge in the world. The latter structure is built of Middlesbrough steel and stands as a worthy example of the capacity of Tees-side's engineers and steel manufacturers.

FIRST YEAR OF NEW TEES BRIDGE

Raised 1,500 Times: Cost 5s 4½d a Lift

The Tees (Newport) Bridge Joint Committee, at their meeting in Middlesbrough yesterday, decided on a precept of £2,885 to each of the constituent authorities — Durham County Council and Middlesbrough Corporation.

The bridgemaster (Mr. Jack Hamilton) reported that he had taken a census of the traffic using the bridge and the average figures for an ordinary day were 1,728 motor vehicles, 4,224 cycles and 2,208 pedestrians.

The bridge has now been open 12 months, he said, and during that time the lifting span has been raised and lowered 1,500 times without any delays of consequence or complaints of any kind. The latter fact, he contended, definitely proved the Committee's contention that the bridge, with its navigation lights, was a help rather than a hindrance to all classes of river users.

5,400 TONS RAISED 99 FEET

Continuing, he said "The cost of the electricity consumed in operating the lifting span, lighting it and the Middlesbrough approach and maintaining the navigation lights is approximately £540, which is equivalent to a cost of 5s 4½d per lift. This is a small figure for raising and lowering a weight of over 5,400 tons for a distance of 99ft. and also maintaining all the necessary lighting.

"Great care and constant supervision over all the electrical and mechanical equipment comprising the operating machinery has been maintained and various small improvements have been made with a view to increasing the reliability of operation."

The local press report on the performance of the new crossing during the first year of operation (The Northern Echo)

They all go Over the Newport Bridge

643 Pedestrians and 943 Vehicles Every Hour

A four days' census of traffic using the Tees Newport Bridge, opened 18 months ago, has been taken. The average daily totals, it was reported to the Bridge Committee at Middlesbrough yesterday, were 2,208 pedestrians, 4,220 cyclists, 1,264 cars, and 595 heavy vehicles.

The maximum hourly totals were 643 pedestrians, 693 cyclists, 157 cars, and 93 heavy transport. The maximum traffic in any single hour was 1,251, and the minimum traffic three.

LITTLE DIFFERENCE

It was stated that the average daily totals revealed little difference when compared with the figures taken in July, 1934, so far as cyclists and pedestrians were concerned, but car and lorry traffic has advanced by 141 or .82 per cent.

The report on the traffic census added that in view of the completion of a large amount of construction at the I.C.I. Works at Billingham since the previous returns were made and the expectation of a reduction in the number of pedestrians and cyclists, the present figures can be considered eminently satisfactory.

"It appears reasonable to suggest," adds the report, "that no great increase can be expected until such time as the connecting road from the end of the Durham approach to Billingham station road is completed."

The Northern Echo shares bridge usage statistics, July 1935

Magnificence in Meccano

In 1935, *Meccano Magazine* featured the world's largest lift bridge on the cover of its April issue, an accolade afforded to internationally acclaimed bridges such as the Brooklyn, Forth, Sydney and Tower Bridges. Starring on the cover alongside the edition dedicating two pages to the story and workings of the Newport Bridge no doubt helped raise the profile of not just the new structure but Middlesbrough.

Locally, Binns combined efforts to sell their goods and perhaps help encourage the wayward children away from causing a nuisance at Newport by instead using the Bridge to sell their goods:

Every boy would like to learn the secrets of the men who built the new Tees Bridge, the Eiffel Tower, the Forth Bridge, the great Harbour Bridge at Sydney, and the many other great engineering wonders of the world. MECCANO makes this possible. With a Meccano Outfit a boy can learn the secret of each one as he builds.

VOL. XX. No. 4. APRIL 1935

MECCANO MAGAZINE

10c WORLD'S LARGEST LIFT BRIDGE
(see page 206)

The April 1935 edition of Meccano Magazine featured the Dorman Long landmark on the cover (Heritage Unlocked Collection)

New Vertical Lift Bridge at Middlesbrough

THE vertical lift bridge across the River Tees at Newport, Middlesbrough, opened in February 1934 by the Duke of York, is the first bridge of this type to be erected in this country, and is claimed to be the largest of its kind in the world. It has a span 265 ft. 4 in. between the bearings of the moving portion, and carries a roadway 38 ft. wide between the kerbs, in addition to two footpaths each 9 ft. in width. When the moving portion is raised for ships to pass, the navigable waterway, which is 250 ft. in width, has a clearance of 120 ft. between high water level and the steelwork of the bridge. When the span is down there is a clearance of 21 ft. The bridge took nearly three years to build and the work cost nearly £500,000, including the cost of the land.

The scheme of which the new bridge forms the principal part has been carried out to the order of a Joint Committee of representatives of the Durham County Council and of the Middlesbrough Corporation, and provides communication between Newport and Haverton Hill Road. This road forms a connection between Stockton-on-Tees and Billingham, and has recently become of increasing importance owing to the industrial development in Billingham and the neighbouring districts.

The illustration above shows the new vertical lift bridge at Middlesbrough in position for vehicles to pass over it. The bridge is the first of the vertical lift type to be built in this country, and is claimed to be the largest of its kind in the world. The photographs illustrating this article are published by courtesy of the engineers, Messrs. Mott, Hay and Anderson.

To effect communication with Haverton Hill Road an approach road was constructed across some low-lying ground on the north side of the river. This approach is carried on an embankment of blast furnace slag for a length of more than 3,000 ft. Half way along the embankment it was found necessary to construct another bridge in order to carry the road across the Billingham Beck branch of the London and North Eastern Railway. This bridge is built of steel, with five spans, and it is the first highway bridge in the country the structural work of which has been erected entirely by welding. On account of the peaty nature of the subsoil, and in order to avoid disturbance of the rail tracks, the five spans of the bridge are supported partly on octagonal reinforced-concrete piles 18 in. in diameter, and partly on 4-in. diameter cylinders, all of which were sunk to a depth of 70 ft. The bridge is 216 ft. in total length, and carries a 38 ft. roadway with a 9 ft. footpath on each side. These widths of roadway and footpath are standard also for the lifting bridge and throughout the approaches.

From the embankment, the lifting span is reached over three approach spans of plate-girder construction, while on the south approach there are two spans of similar construction followed by a 154-ft. span carried on double warren trusses. Continuing along the south approach, there is a reinforced-concrete box abutment, a skew span of 68 ft., and finally a 500-ft. length of embankment on a falling gradient, built between two concrete retaining walls.

The lift span, which weighs 2,700 tons, is suspended from two supporting towers, and is arranged so that it can be lifted and lowered vertically between them to allow boats to pass. To enable the span to be lifted in this way without the necessity for extremely powerful engines, it is provided with four steel counterweight boxes, to which it is connected by means of 80 wire ropes that pass over eight pulley sheaves arranged at the top of the towers. These sheaves are steel castings 15 ft. in diameter, and are mounted on roller bearings and protected against the weather by a number of hoods. The counterweight boxes, which hang vertically, are partly filled with burr concrete, a material in which the customary stone aggregate is replaced by steel punchings; and the remaining part of the weight required is made up of cast iron blocks to enable final adjustments in weight to be made.

The two towers that support the lift span are each 156 ft. in height. As the counterweights exactly balance the span, the towers have to carry a combined moving weight, or load, of 5,400 tons, half of which is taken by

each tower. This load is a vertical one and therefore it is borne by the vertical front legs of the towers, which form guiding surfaces for the ends of the lifting span. The remaining portions of the towers are merely bracing supports for the front legs, and transverse and longitudinal wind bracing.

Each of the towers is supported on a foundation that consists of four cylinders, arranged in two pairs, that have been sunk into the bed of the river to depths varying between 75 ft. and 90 ft. below high water level. The front pair support the two vertical legs just referred to and are of massive construction. The bottom 24 ft. of each of these front cylinders is a steel caisson of 27 ft. diameter that was sunk into position under compressed air. The remainder, or upper portion, consists of a series of cast iron cylindrical segments bolted together and filled with concrete as they were being sunk. The rear pair of cylinders support the curved rear legs of the tower, and as the weight imposed upon them is much less they are smaller, being only 10 ft. in diameter above the bed of the river and 14 ft. in diameter below. The four cylinders are protected from damage by shipping by what are known as "dolphins." These are made of timber and consist of piles sunk into the river, joined by crossbracing and covered with special sheeting.

The bridge is electrically operated from a control cabin slung beneath the machinery cabin which is situated centrally on top of the lift span. The necessary power is obtained from the high-voltage A.C. mains of the Middlesbrough Electricity Department, and is fed to a sub-station built near the south approach to the bridge, where it is transformed to low-voltage current. It is then passed to vertical conductors that extend up the face of the south tower, and collector shoes engaging with them convey the current to the machinery cabin. Inside this cabin it is converted into direct current and is then led to the

A close-up of the lift span showing the machinery house, below which the operator's cabin is situated.

The top of one of the bridge towers, showing the pulleys, which are 15 ft. in diameter, and the hoods to protect them from the weather.

two motors that, through geared shafts, operate the four winding drums. Emergency operating plant for use in the event of a failure of the electricity supply consists of a Thornycroft petrol engine in the machinery cabin, that can drive the drums, and windlasses and gearing for raising and lowering the lift span by hand.

The construction of the vertical lift bridge and its approaches was begun in March 1931, the engineers being Messrs. Mott, Hay and Anderson, of London, S.W.1, and the constructors, Dorman, Long and Co. Ltd.

It is not known when the first vertical lift bridge was built, but during the 19th century several short span bridges of this type were erected across canals in Europe and America. It is interesting to note that one of the earliest really important vertical lift bridges to be planned was intended to span the River Tees near the site of the present structure, but the design was rejected. This proposed bridge had a lifting span 200 ft. long that could be raised 40 ft. and was to be moved up and down by withdrawing water from and adding it to a tank that formed part of the counterweight of the bridge. The first large vertical lift bridge was erected over the South Chicago River at Chicago in 1894. It had a lifting span 130 ft. long which, when raised, provided a vertical clearance of 155 ft.

Some excellent examples of modern vertical lift bridges span the reconstructed Welland Canal in Canada. The height of lift of the bridges ranges from 108 ft. 2 in. to 115 ft. 2 in., and the combined weight of lifting span and counterweight is from 1,036 to 2,054 tons. The width of the bridges is 20 ft. and that of others 30 ft. The bridges vary in minor details, but in general design each consists of two vertical towers and a horizontal span that is moved up and down between them by cables worked from the machinery house at the centre of the span, as is the case with the Middlesbrough bridge.

The Vertical Lift Bridge at Middlesbrough was the subject of a double page Meccano Magazine feature, April 1935 (Heritage Unlocked Collection)

Industrial activity returns to Teesside

The following year *Yorkshire Post* headlines read 'industrial activity returns to Teesside' as the steel manufacturing, the expanding chemical sector and shipbuilding industries all connected by the new bridge enjoyed a period of recovery.

By April 1935 there had been marked progress on the north side of the Tees as the press reported the first shipment of petrol produced by the hydrogenation of creosote at the Billingham plant of ICI, with Ramsay MacDonald performing the plant official inauguration ceremony in October 1935. In the ensuing years, it was quickly apparent that ICI would be at the heart of industrial activity in Teesside and the Newport Bridge would play an important part in the infrastructure of enterprise.

FIRST SHIPMENT OF PETROL FROM BILLINGHAM. Pending the completion of the plant for the direct hydrogenation of coal, the first shipment of petrol, some 300,000 gallons, produced by the hydrogenation of creosote at the Billingham plant of Imperial Chemical Industries, Ltd., was yesterday being loaded into the s.s. Otterhound at Billingham.

A report on the first shipment of petrol from the coal hydrogenation plant at ICI (The Northern Echo)

BILLINGHAM'S NEW INDUSTRY INITIATED

BIG DAY FOR I.C.I.

PETROL FROM COAL PLANT MAKES A START

POSSIBILITIES

GODSEND TO TEES-SIDE AND DURHAM

YESTERDAY was a memorable day in the history of Tees-side industry, for, at Billingham Imperial Chemical Industries, operated for the first time a hydrogenation unit of the petrol plant that is to be engaged in converting coal-tar creosote into petrol. This is the result of seven years' of unremitting laboratory research.

As an indication of the immensity of the project, Sir Harry McGowan, chairman of the I.C.I., in a speech at the last annual meeting of the company, revealed:—

That over £1,000,000 had been spent in research work under process;

The plant cost £2,500,000, and contracts already placed total £1,600,000;

Production will amount to 100,000 tons of petrol per annum; and,

The total employment, direct and indirect, when the plant is in full operation is estimated at 13,600 men.

It is understood that the works have already contracted to market the full output of petrol for some time.

Reports are in circulation that in the early summer plans may be made for extensions to the plant.

FILLIP FOR COALFIELD

Apart from the employment given directly at the I.C.I. Billingham works, much valuable employment will be given to miners in the Durham coalfields, the coal of which has proved entirely suitable for the hydrogenation process.

It is estimated that the production cost of the petrol will be less than 7d per gallon, and, as announced in July, 1933, the Government has given a guarantee that for a number of years the tax on imported petrol will be kept at a 'evel which will enable the home producer to compete with it.

For the expeditious transport of petrol by sea a jetty has been constructed on the river frontage near the Newport Bridge.

It is not expected that the works in operation will immediately give the same amount of employment as they did in construction. The project has meant a substantial increase to the size of the Billingham works, and over £1,000,000 worth of steel work has been used its

construction, the latter including large process departments and petrol storage tanks.

Every effort has been made to ensure safety from fire in the course of production.

The process adopted at Billingham is different from that of the low temperature carbonisation which is to be exploited in connection with the proposed new plant at Seaham Harbour.

"A MODERN MIRACLE"

Professor Low has termed hydrogenation a modern miracle. To trade-depressed Tees-side it has been a God-send.

Tees-siders may recall that as early as 1931 Billingham scientists had discovered a coal-petrol with which they were able to run motor-cars. Since then research has been rigorously pursued to make this home-produced petrol a marketable proposition.

In the event of a war-time emergency the home-produced spirit will be of immense value as a fuel to aircraft and the increasing number of Naval vessels which have been converted from coal to oil-users.

Lord Londonderry (Minister of Air) recently mentioned to the "Gazette" that a squadron of R.A.F. 'planes was already using the new coal-produced petrol.

It is anticipated that at least 850,000 tons of coal will be treated per annum, this amount to increase as the plant is extended. The plant has taken a year and a half to build.

SIR HARRY McGOWAN, chairman of Imperial Chemical Industries.

Work commences at the petrol from coal plant at ICI, 9th February 1935 (North Eastern Daily Gazette)

The value of the new bridge as an alternative means of crossing the river when the Transporter Bridge was out of action was also apparent in 1936 when the older crossing was temporarily out of action when a wire rope had broken and traffic had to be diverted to the Newport crossing.

A new road scheme on the north side of the Tees, supported by a grant from the Ministry of Transport, commenced in 1937 and improvement works on the Middlesbrough approach were carried out with the introduction of a traffic island to help manage traffic flow. The new road would connect the approach road northward towards Billingham Bank removing the need for drivers to negotiate the difficult route through the industrial developments at Billingham. The coming of the Second World War in 1939 threatened to derail the scheme like many capital schemes elsewhere but the Ministry of Transport authorised the continuation of works.

The official opening of the new plant at Billingham by Ramsay MacDonald (The Northern Echo)

Work on the approaches to the Newport Bridge continued in 1937 (North Eastern Daily Gazette)

A new traffic island nears completion in 1937 (North Eastern Daily Gazette)

The Second World War and Post-War Teesside

"Faced with the prospect of paying out £60,000 for new ropes to lift Newport Bridge, plus an annual upkeep bill of £20,000, the committee that controls the Bridge is considering closing it to river traffic."

Evening Gazette, 5th August 1967

The Second World War brought major changes to Teesside, not least for the industries along the River Tees that worked to supply chemicals, ships and steel for use in the conflict. Throughout the period, the Tees Newport Bridge continued to operate and played a key role in supporting the infrastructure of Teesside's industries as the region rallied behind the war effort.

Air raid shelters, rockets and a Royal return

A number of precautions were taken to protect the local community and infrastructure around the Newport Bridge. Specially constructed public air raid shelters were erected in the shadow of Newport Bridge in October 1939 and were described as a 'strange sight' in the local press.

The recollections of Sidney Clay reveal activity around Newport Bridge during the Second World War, including a hit on nearby gas tanks that illuminated the sky and the establishment of an anti-aircraft rocket site near Newport Bridge. He also recalls soldiers operating smoke producing equipment mounted on lorries on the road between Billingham and the crossing that during alerts would light combustion chambers to produce thick black smoke that provided a smokescreen for the Tees' industries. Another memory submitted to the BBC's WW2 People's War project described barrage balloons in the vicinity of Newport Bridge and bombs dropped in 1940 that brought death and destruction with families killed, homes destroyed and many injured.

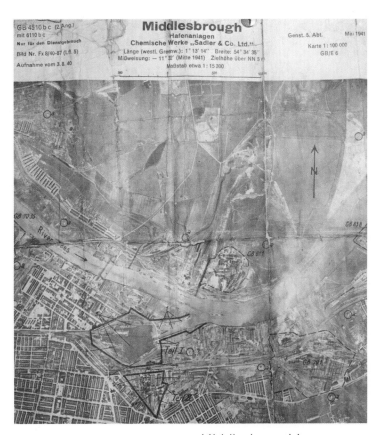

Middlesbrough's industries were subject to aerial bombardment during the Second World War (British Steel Collection, Teesside Archives)

In 1941, two familiar faces made a fleeting return to the Tees Newport Bridge when the King and Queen – formerly the Duke and Duchess of York – concluded a tour of the North East with a visit to Middlesbrough and entered Yorkshire from Durham via the crossing en route to a parade of the branches of local civil defence services at Albert Park. Sadly, the same year brought a fatality on the bridge when Finnish seaman Yrjö Luotonen was hit by a lorry.

As the Second World War drew to a close, works were carried out to replace ropes on Newport Bridge. In 1945, Middlesbrough played host to 25 Polish soldiers who visited the town's two iconic bridges before having tea at the Seamen's Mission as guests of the Rotary Club.

Just as the Transporter Bridge had endured despite suffering damage during an aerial bombardment, the Newport Bridge survived the air raids to stand witness to the postwar decades that brought rapid change to the local economy, transformed the skyline and called into question the continued existence of the Tees' two most iconic bridges.

Post-war peril

The post-war years proved to be challenging for the Newport crossing with a number of concerns, calamities and transport chaos adding to calls for a conventional bridge. In 1946, the Newport crossing was in the news when the rear offside wheel of a wagon carrying fairground equipment collapsed as the vehicle was running off the bridge. According to one newspaper report, 'wooden horses and other fairground equipment were strewn about the road' before the vehicle and its crew were elevated above the Tees as the lifting span cleared the way for shipping! It was another two hours before the calamity was cleared and the wagon was repaired.

By 1947, Max Lock's *The County Borough of Middlesbrough Survey and Plan* was published that made several recommendations for town planning that would, according to Mayor of Middlesbrough L.G. Allen, ensure the town would 'avoid many of the mistakes of the past' and take the necessary action to ensure Middlesbrough could 'become the residential, cultural and shopping centre for Tees-side'. The Newport Bridge was referenced in several parts of the publication, including one assessment that the new link had 'destroyed the dominance of Stockton as the regional route-centre, and has given Middlesbrough the possibility of extending its regional influence northwards at the expense of Stockton'. The Lock-led study also contended that 'the bridging of the Tees at the Newport roundabout has given alternative choice of occupation to over 3,000 Middlesbrough wage earners' and also asked the question as to why the town's two landmark bridges could not be painted with brighter colours!

A postwar scene - G.S Cooper's artwork of No.1655 alongside the elevated Newport Bridge (Paul Stephenson Collection)

The Newport Bridge featured in Max Lock's Middlesbrough Survey and Plan.

The Max Lock survey recognised the infrastructure value of Newport Bridge and suggested brighter colours for the structure.

Tragedy, industrial change and safety concerns

The late 1940s through to the 1960s brought extensive changes to the industrial infrastructure and skyline on the south bank of the Tees. The former Newport Ironworks site and surrounding ironworks had been cleared and the research laboratories were the focus of Dorman Long's activity on the site. In 1949 the Eston Ironstone Mine closed, the 1950s saw the last cast at Britannia Works and in the ensuing decades the focus of Dorman Long – and later British Steel – was on developments downstream at Lackenby and Redcar rather than at Middlesbrough.

A view of the Dorman Long landmark from the firm's Central Research Laboratory (British Steel Collection, Teesside Archives)

The Tees Newport Bridge provides an impressive backdrop to Dorman Long's Central Research Laboratory, 1947 (British Steel Collection, Teesside Archives)

COUNTY BOROUGH OF
MIDDLESBROUGH

ERIMUS

MIDDLESBROUGH ENGLAND

TEES - SIDE'S REGIONAL CENTRE — INDUSTRIAL SITES AVAILABLE
FOR INFORMATION APPLY TO THE TOWN CLERK

In the 1950s the Newport Bridge competed with the Transporter Bridge as an icon and symbol of Middlesbrough as it usurped the 'flying ferry' on Middlesbrough Handbook and local authority promotional literature. Whether this was due to the increased centrality of the newer bridge in the industrial life of the area or was simply for a change from the norm we cannot be certain.

By the 1960s, the blocks which formed the original roadway of the span were considered unsuitable for fastmoving traffic - particularly when wet – and were replaced in 1966 with new blocks with an anti-skid dressing to the surface. The move came shortly after tragedy stuck on the bridge when a lorry driver and his passenger sadly lost their lives after the vehicle skidded from the road and plunged into the Tees.

The Newport Bridge featured in an advertisement for the County Borough of Middlesbrough in 1950 (Middlesbrough Libraries)

MIDDLESBROUGH

OFFICIAL HANDBOOK

The Newport Bridge featured on the cover of the Middlesbrough Official Handbook in the 1950s (Middlesbrough Libraries)

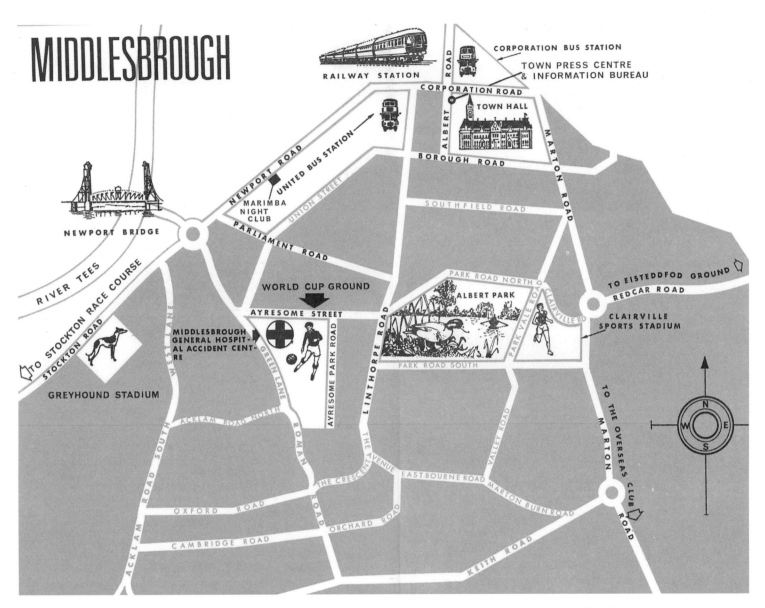

MIDDLESBROUGH

RAILWAY STATION

CORPORATION BUS STATION

TOWN PRESS CENTRE & INFORMATION BUREAU

CORPORATION ROAD

TOWN HALL

BOROUGH ROAD

NEWPORT ROAD

UNITED BUS STATION

MARIMBA NIGHT CLUB

UNION STREET

SOUTHFIELD ROAD

NEWPORT BRIDGE

PARLIAMENT ROAD

RIVER TEES

TO STOCKTON RACE COURSE

STOCKTON ROAD

WORLD CUP GROUND

AYRESOME STREET

MIDDLESBROUGH GENERAL HOSPIT- AL ACCIDENT CENT- RE

PARK ROAD NORTH

ALBERT PARK

TO EISTEDDFOD GROUND

REDCAR ROAD

CLAIRVILLE RD

CLAIRVILLE SPORTS STADIUM

PARK ROAD SOUTH

GREEN LANE

LINTHORPE ROAD

AYRESOME PARK ROAD

PARK VALE ROAD

MARTON ROAD

GREYHOUND STADIUM

WEST LANE

ACKLAM ROAD NORTH

ROMAN ROAD

ACKLAM ROAD SOUTH

OXFORD ROAD

THE CRESCENT

THE AVENUE

EASTBOURNE ROAD

VALLEY ROAD

MARTON BURN ROAD

TO THE OVERSEAS CLUB

MARTON ROAD

ORCHARD ROAD

CAMBRIDGE ROAD

KEITH ROAD

N
W E
S

The Dorman Long landmark featured in the 'Welcome to Middlesbrough' guide produced for the 1966 World Cup

Despite improvement works, the landmark faced further problems. The Evening Gazette '£60,000 shock on the bridge' headline from March 1967 was a sign of costly challenges to come for local authorities in the ensuing decade. The large fee for renewing the lifting and haulage ropes of the bridge coupled with consultants recommending the works should take place within a year rather than spread over several years stunned the Tees (Newport) Bridge Joint Committee, who had budgeted only £10,600 for work to be carried out in the coming year. Nevertheless, the Committee agreed to the works with Chairman Alderman Fred Longstaff stating 'I got a shock when I read this report. I would not like the public to get the impression, however, that the bridge is unsafe'. Councillor J.A. Bell echoed the sentiments, remarking 'we cannot afford to ignore the advice of our consultants on this; it is urgent'.

The decline in lifts

Despite the apparent urgency to carry out repairs on the Bridge, by June 1967 work had been postponed following news that Stockton Quay would no longer be used for shipping. The move called the future of lifting the structure into question as the industrial dynamics of the River Tees changed with the Newport Bridge at the heart of this shift. The move prompted the Electric Trades Union to express concern over the future of its members who controlled the working of the bridge and would likely find their jobs under threat if they no longer had to elevate the span.

The question of costs and the reduced frequency of lifts of the main span were debated in the press, with it revealed the structure was costing ratepayers £30,000 a year and had lifted just 19 times in May 1967 compared to 23 times during the same period a year earlier. By August 1967, the Joint Bridge Committee had decided to call a meeting with local authorities and key stakeholders to make the case that the time was opportune for closing the bridge to river traffic, with Chairman Longstaff arguing:

> We would be paying a lot of money out for this on the possibility that one or two industries might want to float something down the river. I am sure there are other means of transport.

Whilst Longstaff's committee were prioritising concerns of the ratepayer, no longer lifting the span posed the potential of job losses at two of the Tees' historic firms – the engineering company Head Wrightson and Ashmore, Benson, Pease and Co., manufacturers of a range of industrial plant including blast furnaces and gas holders.

Newport Bridge may close to river traffic

FACED with the prospect of paying out £60,000 for new ropes to lift Newport Bridge, plus an annual upkeep bill of £20,000, the committee that controls the bridge is considering closing it to river traffic.

But before making the decision the committee — the Tees (Newport) Bridge Joint Committee — is to consult Thornaby and Stockton councils.

Alarm bells sounded for the readers of the *Evening Gazette* on 17th October 1967 as they were met with the headline 'HEAD WRIGHTSON WARNING...2,000 jobs hang on bridge ropes'. Head Wrightson Secretary James Iveson urged a meeting of key stakeholders that 'we must not, whatever happened, prejudice the jobs of these people'. Alderman C. Anderton of Thornaby said no longer lifting the Bridge would sterilise upriver industry, Norman Sellars, Deputy General Manager of the Tees and Hartlepool Port Authority, argued that such a move would prevent maintenance along the river, whilst the Ministry of Transport expressed concern at Head Wrightson moving big loads by road.

For now, the lifting function was reprieved and by 1968 work had begun on the renewal of the lift and haulage ropes, resulting in closure of the Bridge from 7-8pm Monday to Saturday and 6am-2pm on selected Sunday to allow for rope repair works. Traffic chaos ensued for evening motorists who were diverted via Thornaby but, nevertheless, the works ensured that large river traffic would still be able to navigate the Tees above Newport.

This 1969 aerial view of the former Newport Ironworks site highlights changes that had occurred to the industrial skyline (Middlesbrough Libraries)

Deindustrialisation and the 'Bridge of Sighs'

"Britain's first and the world's highest vertical lift bridge has become well-nigh redundant, a gaunt monument to the time tall ships passed beneath...Its popularity as a spectacle, too, seems to have declined in recent years. Once children and their parents would take time out to watch our very own world-beater swing into action, but not anymore."

Evening Gazette Teeslife Supplement, 25th September 1979

An estimated 45,000 vehicles per day crossed the Newport Bridge in 1970 as moves progressed towards the construction of a Tees Viaduct that would relieve the strain on the lift bridge and ultimately replace it as the main crossing of the Tees for vehicles.

The 1970s proved to be a troubled decade for the Newport Bridge as its importance declined amidst deindustrialisation, failed regeneration schemes and problems with the operation of the structure.

Artist's impression of the Tees Viaduct by Messrs Dobbie, Sandford, Fawcett, Partners Consultant Engineers

TEES-SIDE INDUSTRIAL DEVELOPMENT BOARD

The challenges caused by the span's roadway returned as the road blocks introduced in the previous decade brought new problems when waterlogged by heavy rain. On one particularly rainy day in July 1974, the crossing was temporarily closed to traffic after blocks moved up and down owing to the passage of vehicles. The *Evening Gazette* headline read 'Bridge 'wash out' leads to Tees Traffic chaos' and tailbacks to Wilderness Road resulted in 'one of the worst snarl-ups the area has known' that left thousands of people later for work and led many to abandon their cars. In November 1974, the blocks were removed and replaced with a hot rolled asphalt which posed its own problems as it increased the weight on the span which meant a similar weight had to be added to the counterweights to maintain the fine balance of the Bridge.

The chaos of that wet July day in 1974 underlined the susceptibility of the structure and vulnerability to traffic chaos when the crossing was out of use. Upriver from the Dorman Long landmark – predictably dubbed the 'bridge of sighs' by one *Evening Gazette* writer - work had been delayed on the new 52-span Tees Viaduct that eventually opened to traffic in November 1975. Carrying the A19, the Tees Viaduct quickly established itself as the main route for crossing the Tees, quickly surpassing the traffic numbers carried on the Newport Bridge. Even then, the Tees Viaduct faced its own problems as it required extensive refurbishment work just over a decade after opening and faced more issues in the 1990s owing to corroded reinforcements in the piers.

The derelict riverside jetty on the former Newport Ironworks site (John Severs)

Inset: Dereliction on the Newport Ironworks site (John Severs)

Newport Bridge viewed from Fox Head's Bridge, c.1970s (John Severs)

Below right: The elevation of Newport Bridge was an increasingly rare sight in the 1970s and 1980s (Paul Sherwood)

Below left: The Dorman Long landmark viewed from the ruins of the ironworks (John Severs)

'Our Sad Monument'

Despite such troubles, in 1976 there was some excitement around Newport Bridge when one notable lift took place as the paddle steamer 'John H Amos' (renamed 'Hero') departed from Stockton for a new life at a maritime museum, with hundreds of people lining the banks of the Tees to say farewell.

The following year the landmark was not elevated once for river traffic, whilst reconstruction work meant the road was once again out of action to motor vehicles – this time for the removal of high-level scaffolding – although pedestrians and cyclists were permitted to use the crossing.

In September 1979, a special *Evening Gazette Teeslife* Supplement reflected on the changing face of the industrial river and its surrounds, the challenges faced by the two landmark bridges connecting Middlesbrough and the north bank and efforts to clean up the Tees. Although highlighting the world record status of the structure, Alan Hepworth's article's 'Our Sad Monument' headline set the tone for a piece that painted a grim picture of reduced staffing numbers and declining local interest. Interviewing Ian MacDonald, described as a tradesman driver on the Bridge, the article provided an insight into a typical week working on the structure, which included Sunday efficiency lifts and checks on electrical installations, cleaning exposed copper bars and carrying out "in house" painting. MacDonald also revealed that he felt 'like a stationmaster still working at a station that has been axed', reflecting:

> It was interesting work when I started but the novelty tends to wear off when the only lifts you do are check ones. The Bridge doesn't take up as much time as it used to and the team can be working on other bridges in the county for the best part of some weeks.

Despite the doom and gloom, the article hinted that the romance of the lifting landmark had not been lost on everyone, noting 'locals may have become blasé, but visitors to Cleveland sometimes swell the small numbers watching the ten-minute operation from either side of the Tees'. This juxtaposition of the romance of engineering against the economic and industrial realities of operating the bridge would be a constant theme in the ensuing decade.

The John H Amos returns, renamed Hero, passes by the Tees Newport Bridge in 1976 (John Severs)

The last decade of lifting

Question marks over the efficiency and economic viability of elevating the roadway became more pressing in the 1980s. A document dating from the late 1980s in Teesside Archives' collection provides a useful insight into the decline in the number of lifts:

> The frequency of requests for the Bridge to be lifted had declined in recent years. To all intents and purposes there has been no need to lift the span in the three years other than for the County Fire Boat on exercise and for members of the Castlegate Marine Yacht Club immediately following disclosure of the proposals to cease operation of the Bridge.

In 1981, only a few lifts for small yachts were noted and the early 1980s brought the last recorded lift for commercial purposes with the departure of a new luxury cruiser built at Stockton before boatbuilding upriver ceased. In September 1980 at a meeting of Cleveland County Council's Highways & Transportation Committee, County Engineer Garth Drabble outlined the decline from 1,700 lifts for river traffic per year in the later 1930s compared to no lifts in 1977 and only around 18 in the ensuing three years. Drabble suggested talks should be opened up with trade unions about introducing day-shift, five day working in place of the existing 7am-7pm manned overlapping shifts that were currently in operation.

This 1982 aerial view of Newport Bridge reflects the vast changes that occurred following deindustrialisation along parts of the Tees (Teesside Archives)

With the local authority cuts of the 1980s coupled with limited lifts, debates around abandoning the lifting mechanism and utilising the structure as only a fixed bridge intensified. At the end of 1981 headlines read 'Costs threaten to keep bridge down' and 'Bridge may be 'fixed'' as the local authority met once again and revealed maintenance of ropes would cost around £300,000 in the next four years. A special report in the *Evening Gazette* by Alan Sims in January 1982 recognised the historic significance and grandeur of the 'great landmark, a steel monster that stands like some magnificent Meccano model' but considered the lack of its practical need to fulfil its lifting function as 'the real problem':

> The old gentleman's party trick is becoming too expensive. It's hardly worth the money and it could well be time for retirement.

'The final act of killing off the Tees'

Following consultations around possible closure as a lifting bridge, there were 24 lifts for yachts between June and September 1982 and debates rumbled on with Stockton's Policy and Resources Committee canvassing local businesses about fixing the roadway in position whilst Middlesbrough councillors insisted the lifting span should 'retain its present character and structures and its operational capacity'. Middlesbrough's councillors were not alone as Head Wrightson contended any fixing of the bridge would be 'the final act of killing off the Tees'. By the end of the year, the costs of fixing the bridge and considerable opposition to the plan saw the proposal abandoned – for now. However, one part of the Bridge that was retired was the 1.52 Thorneycroft engine, the standby power unit to lift the main span. The redundant 12 cylinder engine – thought to be the only one remaining in existence - was gifted to the Maritime Museum at Gosport.

Celebrating half a century

Between 1983-85 there were approximately six lifts per year for yachts either side of Summer Bank Holidays. Yet, the limited use of the lift function failed to dampen the spirits of those arranging the Tees River Festival of 1984 which would mark Newport Bridge's 50th year. The half-century of opening on 28th February passed by without any notable celebrations. *The Northern Echo* took a cake along to the Newport Bridge for Stockton's Mayor to blow out the candles and there were a few feature articles that shared personal stories about the steel icon. One such tale was that of 68-year-old John Linton who reminisced about his first job as a teenager operating the lifting span of the bridge, a role that required an 'interview' consisting of a climb up and down the metal-runged ladder to the top of the structure – the alternative option to the access lift to the top of the towers!

The Newport Bridge featured on the cover of Middlesbrough News in 1984

The main celebrations took the form of the Tees River Festival on Sunday 24th June, consisting of a programme of races, displays of working and pleasure craft on the Tees and, of course, a lift of the star of the show. Perhaps the Tees River Festival would have been the perfect time to bow out as a lift bridge as the remainder of the decade brought several well-documented incidents where either the span failed to lift or got stuck elevated above the 'Steel River'.

In 1986 there were once again no lifts for river traffic and the following year the only two recorded lifts were part of a County Fire Boat exercise in March. The closure of Head Wrightson removed any industrial case for retaining the lifting function. In 1988 several lifts were facilitated for yachts following renewed consultation with the Yacht Club about possible closure of the lift span but the party trick was on borrowed time. Despite, or perhaps because of, this the structure was Grade II listed in July 1988 in recognition of its special architectural and historical interest.

A Bridge's Birthday, 1984 (Middlesbrough News & Paul Stephenson)

MIDDLESBROUGH NEWS FEB 1984

A BRIDGE'S BIRTHDAY

One of Cleveland's best-known landmarks, the Newport Lift Bridge, is fifty years old this month. The opening ceremony was performed in 1934 by the then Duke of York, the future King George VI.

To mark the anniversary a leaflet outlining the bridge's history and technical specification has been published by the County Council - and later this year the Newport Bridge is to get a new coat of paint.

When it was built the Bridge was the largest of its type in the world and was regarded as a tribute to the skill of its builders, the Middlesbrough firm of Dorman Long & Company. The opening ceremony concluded a project which had begun in 1920 when eighteen local councils on Teesside got together to improve road communications in the area with a view to future industrial development.

At that time the main river crossing was the Transporter Bridge, and local businessmen were pressing for a more efficient road route, preferably a tunnel under the Tees.

However, then - just as more recently - a tunnel was ruled out because the local authorities were worried about the cost involved. Instead they opted for a bridge which would still leave the river clear for the the busy shipping upriver to Stockton Quay - and the designers came up with the novel proposal for a lifting bridge, at a price of £512,000.

These days the Newport Bridge electric winding gear is called on to raise the 5,000 ton roadway platform an average of twelve times a year, chiefly for pleasure craft based at Stockton. The cost of maintaining the bridge is met by Cleveland County Council.

With hindsight, it must be questioned how right the civic leaders concerned were to choose another mechanical bridge to add to the Transporter. The construction project certainly brought a welcome order to the local steelworks - but Teesside could have had a tunnel under the River Tees as long ago as 1910. Earlier this year a plan for a Tees Tunnel was shelved until the next century.

FACT FILE | E. Gazette 25.11.85 | *Heritage*

Newport Bridge

● Location: Spanning the River Tees between Newport on the Middlesbrough side and Portrack at Stockton.

● Statistics: Built 51 years ago, the bridge weighs in at 12,000 tons and stands 182ft 2in high. The moveable central span weighs 2,700 tons and is moved by machinery housed in the towers. Now moved only one or two times a year, the heyday of the Bridge came in the days when ships were able to navigate to the jetties inland towards Stockton.

● History: Opened by the Duke of York 51 years ago, the Bridge was built by Dorman Long as the main crossing point for the river. Built during the depression of the thirties, it was also intended to provide work for the thousands of jobless in the area and to demonstrate the engineering skills which were available. At the time, it was the biggest Bridge of its type ever to be seen in Britain and had cost £512,000 to build.

● Today: Even after 50 years and after the building of a flyover a few hundred yards away, Newport Bridge is still one of the main crossing points on the River — as was borne out recently when the Bridge was closed for a number of weeks to allow maintenance to be carried out.

Strange world record holder

IT is the world's highest vertical lift bridge, a masterpiece of complex machinery, steel chains, steel ropes and gangways.

It works superbly well. But the trouble is it never really needs to. Well, hardly ever, anyway.

Newport Bridge is one of a pair of strange world record-holders within an amazingly short stretch of the Tees at Middlesbrough.

The other is, of course, the Transporter Bridge, which carries people and cars across the murky river on a hanging platform ... the only one of its kind still operating this swinging-style of ferry service.

But whereas part of the Transporter's fame is the regular way it breaks down, the story behind the Newport Bridge is how rarely it is called on to operate at all.

It weighs in at 12,000 tons, it stands 182ft 2in, it's 51 years old, it costs thousands of pounds a year to run, and it is now asked to lift its hefty 2,700-ton central span only to allow private yachts to pass with their tall masts ... about twice a year at the most.

There was a time when Newport Bridge was called on 30 times a month to allow bulk-carrying ships through. This was before the closure of Stockton Quay, and the slow-down of river traffic beneath its clumsy frame.

But as a novelty, it's a gem, and it's nice to have around, even if the team only lift it on Sundays for efficiency reasons. And even if it has been likened to a railway station with no trains.

It was the first vertical lift bridge to be opened in this country. And it was a proud town that gathered on February 28, 1934, to watch that opening by King George VI, who was then Duke of York.

It cost just over half-a-million pounds, and is a masterly engineering job, with 160 steel ropes capable of pulling the span 99 feet up — giving it a clearance of 120 feet.

The project was another major achievement for Dorman Long of Middlesbrough, to stand alongside the Sydney Harbour Bridge in Australia, Lambeth and Putney Bridges in London and Siam's Memorial Bridge.

And though its particular talents are not needed so much now, the Newport Bridge did work all right. In fact, there was one day when it started working on its own. The main motor generator in the machinery house suddenly set off.

But it was discovered that it had just been some clumsy jackdaw which had dropped a piece of wire across the connectors.

Anyway, here we have in one town two bridges which seem as eccentrically out of time as they are masterfully made.

The end of an era

The death knell sounded for romantics of industrial engineering and lovers of the peculiar spectacle of the lifting span with the decision made to apply for the repeal of the Parliamentary Act that placed a legal obligation on the local authority to lift the landmark for river traffic. In 1989 at the third reading of the Bill, Stockton North MP Frank Cook made the case for repealing the obligation:

> The machinery and other equipment required to facilitate the raising of the bridge is very expensive to maintain and given the fact that the bridge... is unlikely to be raised again, the financial burden imposed on the county council is considerable and can no longer by justified. If the statutory

obligation to raise the bridge can be repealed, the council estimates that it will save approximately £1 million over the next 10 years. I assure the House that, even with the bridge in its lowered position, there is approximately 6m clearance for vessels at high water. That compares with a clearance of 5m for the Victoria Bridge upriver at Stockton and a minimum clearance of 5.5m for the proposed new road bridge which would be constructed if and when the River Tees Barrage and Crossing Bill is enacted. I commend this Bill unreservedly to the House.

Royal Assent to the Bill was given on 3rd July 1989 and the Tees (Newport) Bridge Act 1989 stating that the legal requirement to lift the bridge had been repealed, became operative on 3rd September 1989.

Doug Hawkes enjoys a breath of fresh air near Newport Bridge

Doorstep delights

THE rises and falls of Teesside's Newport Bridge may be coming to an end, but riverside recreation is definitely on the up.

That's the view of Doug Hawkes, who as River Tees warden will be trying to promote public awareness and enjoyment of open spaces, industrial heritage and wildlife along Cleveland's "Tees corridor".

Many people, he says, enjoy trips into the countryside, but do not realise the opportunities on their own doorsteps.

A Tees Path, now being developed, will make it possible to walk across Cleveland, beside the river, from one side of the county to the other.

A former North Wales planner and teacher in a rural school in Sumatra, Mr Hawkes earlier worked as a countryside ranger in an urban fringe of West London.

A snapshot of the Newport crossing just months before the last lift (Evening Gazette)

The 1980s brought a new emphasis on riverside recreation, as found in this 1988 article (The Northern Echo)

The last official lift of the main span took place on Sunday 18th November 1990 as Teesside marked the end of an era. In the week leading up to the event the local press declared:

> It will be an historic day on Teesside on Sunday when Newport Bridge across the River Tees is raised for the last time. Afterwards, the green bridge, one of the best known landmarks in the area, will be permanently fixed down. There will be three lifts of the bridge – around noon – so that everyone interested in taking photographs or video film of the event can be accommodated. Built in 1934, the bridge has rarely been lifted in recent years, and is being fixed down because of escalating costs.

County Council Chairman, Councillor Ted Wood, said he hoped as many people as possible would come along to see the last lift and he was not to be disappointed as Teessiders and visitors from across the country turned out in their droves.

Footage of the last lift can be found in the collections of Teesside Archives and shows dozens of people gathered on the elevated main span and hundreds more lining the banks of the Tees to witness the final lift of this groundbreaking feat of engineering excellence.

Geoff Taylor, then Tees Pilot, remembers the day well:

> The final time the Bridge was raised I was fortunate enough to receive an invitation to the celebration or commiserations. Taking my son Tim, who was then about eight, we enjoyed watching the tugs with fire hoses spouting and the Tees fire boat similarly spray as the bridge was ceremonially raised and lowered. The police then began directing most of the Bridge's occupants off the roadway for the final lift which was to hold only those wearing chains of office. We were standing close to a lady with a fine set of mayoral regalia so I moved closer to her taking Tim with me. Assuming us to be her partners, we were not ushered off and we thus enjoyed the final lift. Afterwards as we walked away, I remember telling Tim he needed to lock the memory away because one day in the distant future he would probably be the last person to have stood on the Newport Bridge as it was raised and lowered - and he probably will be!

Just as the Duchess and Duke of York had done some 20, 718 days earlier, a small number of visitors were able to share a part of history and enjoy a unique vantage point of a now much-changed Teesside from the elevated main span and with it, reflect on the end of an era.

Life after Lifting

"Newport Bridge is a spectacular structure with a proud and fascinating history, and it dominates the skyline above the River Tees. The new lighting shows the bridge at its very best and anyone passing it after sunset is in for a real treat."

Stockton-on-Tees Council Leader, Councillor Bob Cook, 2017

Since that last lift in 1990, Teesside has experienced significant change as the industrial landscape of the 'Steel River' has been transformed and several new bridges have been built across the Tees upriver from the 1934 structure. Despite the extensive changes experienced in the late twentieth and early decades of the twenty first century, the Newport Bridge remained an important part of local transport infrastructure and like the rest of Teesside, has experienced turbulent times and some positive transformation.

The Newport Bridge painted blue in February 1993 (The Gazette)

Closures and colours

Troubled times for the neighbouring Transporter Bridge in recent decades has seen the cross-Tees link closest to the mouth of the river closed several times for periods of over a year owing to a combination of repair work, renovation and repainting schemes. Most recently, safety concerns have rendered the 'flying ferry' closed for five years and led to question marks over the very future of the Transporter Bridge owing to economic considerations and the feasibility of the 1911 structure dealing with the demands of traffic in the 2020s and beyond. In comparison, the Tees Newport Bridge has fared well as a conventional road bridge and helped relieve some of the transport pressure caused by the older icon's closures, albeit in the early 1990s the Newport crossing too underwent closures to allow for fixing down of the structure as well as carrying out repainting and remedial works.

In May 1998, it was announced that ahead of the repainting of the Newport Bridge that summer Stockton Council would invite members of the public to help select the colour of the paint job, with Vice-Chair of Stockton Council's development Committee recognising the importance of the crossing on the skyline:

> Newport Bridge is an important landmark and has a major visual impact on Teesside. Thousands of people use it every day and this is a great opportunity for them to have a say in its final colour. The Bridge was originally painted a shade of dark green when it first opened in 1934. I would like to see it restored to that colour and we have put that forward as our preferred option. But before we make our decision we would like to know what the users think. We would be delighted to consider a range of other options.

A bus travels across the Newport Bridge in 1993 (The Gazette)

Posters showing how the landmark would look in different colour schemes were displayed in municipal buildings and the town's central library alongside voting slips. It was ultimately decided that a return to its original green colour should be pursued. To the frustration of the 30,000 drivers per day using the crossing, another closure of several months followed between August and November 1998 as the structure was repainted from blue to green. In November 1998, local residents were invited to take a closer look at the paint job and enjoy a rare visit to the control room and engine house.

The next transformative repainting and refurbishment of Newport Bridge would take place in 2014 – the 80th anniversary of the official opening - when the historic green colour was replaced with a red and silver colour scheme. However, the project experienced severe delays owing to the discovery of damage to the Grade II listed structure, with some 40% of the steelwork estimated to be suffering from corrosion. The discoveries saw costs rise from £1.6m to £4.6m and initial repainting and repair works that had been scheduled to last a few months were instead replaced by more extensive interventions.

A makeover of the landmark commenced in 2014 (The Gazette)

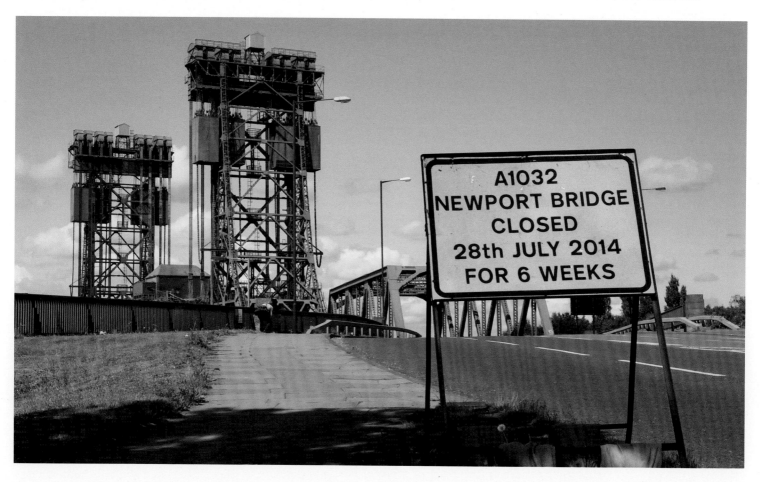

Whilst the A1032 – the road that crosses Newport Bridge - was able to reopen to traffic in October 2014 courtesy of a birdcage scaffold that allowed work to continue above and around the motor vehicles using the link, the new works programme was not completed until the following year. At the time of writing, the same colour scheme remains although this has faded somewhat over the past decade. With local authority cutbacks and the significant costs associated with repainting the gigantic structure, it may be some time before a new colour scheme is introduced.

Richard McGuckin of Stockton-on-Tees Borough Council pictured underneath the scaffolding works in 2014 (The Gazette)

The repainting work revealed some of the colours the bridge had previously been painted (The Gazette)

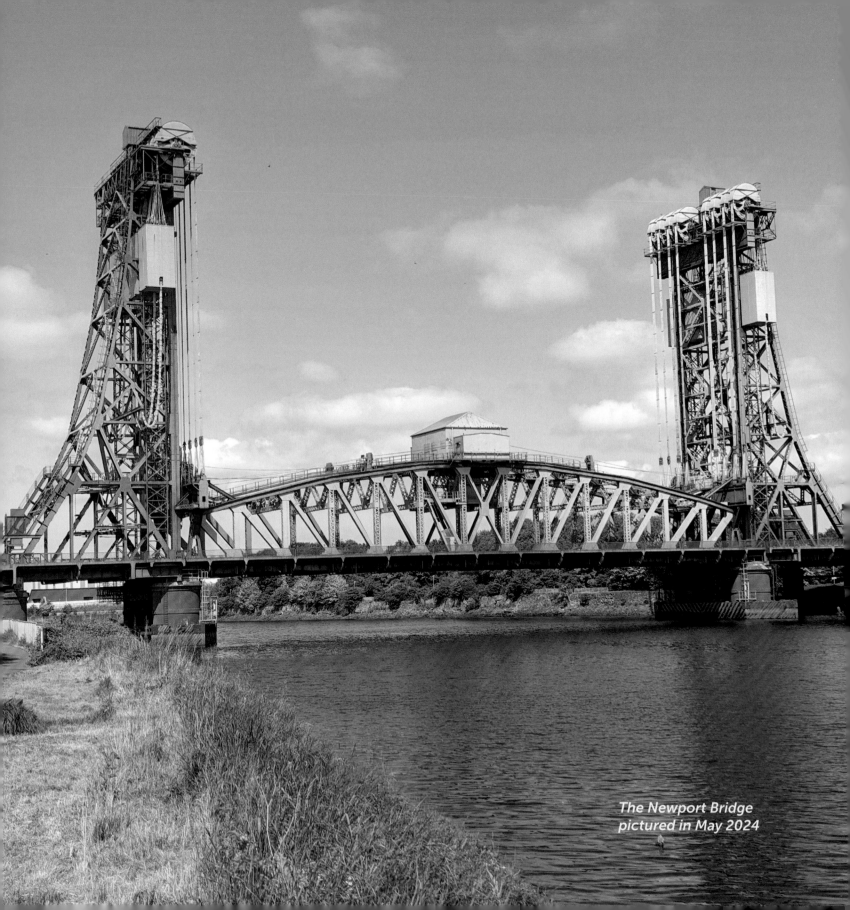

*The Newport Bridge
pictured in May 2024*

Art, heritage and culture of the Newport Bridge

Despite pre-1990 users of the Newport Bridge no doubt having flashbacks of traffic chaos occasioned by the elevation of the Dorman Long landmark's span, many Teessiders have a fondness for their bridges that is reflected in art, heritage and cultural activity in the area.

In 1994, the Newport Bridge featured alongside Yarm High Street, the cliffs at Saltburn and Roseberry Topping on a series of fundraising Christmas Cards sold in aid of Teesside Hospice to underline the landmark quality. In 1996, the abolition of Cleveland County Council meant the Newport Bridge disappeared from local authority logos and the new logos of Middlesbrough Council have since only found space to adapt the Transporter Bridge into their branding.

Curiously, the long, drawn-out debates that surrounded the building of the Newport crossing by competing local authorities in the interwar years were referenced in 1993 campaign literature calling for the 1990s Cleveland area to continue to operate as one local authority. Beyond logos, local authority changes meant that agreement had to be reached on the management and maintenance of the two historic bridges over the Tees and it was decided that Middlesbrough Borough Council would have responsibility for the Transporter Bridge and Stockton-on-Tees the Newport Bridge with each authority making financial and contributions where relevant.

Despite disappearing from local authority branding, the Newport Bridge has been celebrated by artists, photographs and creative interpretations across the decades. One of the most apparent has been through the continued enthusiasm for recreating the elevated bridge in Meccano. In 1997, retired engineer Arthur Clark created his Meccano working model in three months using some 800 nuts and bolts. The 77-year-old was well-qualified to recreate the model that went on display in Billingham's Kingsway House as not only did Clark previously work for the Middlesbrough steel firm but he also remembered the Bridge's construction:

> I lived in Ayresome Grange Road and I actually saw it being built as a boy. I have always been mechanically-minded. I used to build all sorts of things out of bits of board and wire.

In 2012 Festival of the North East featured another Meccano model of Newport Bridge and across the decades various other creations inspired by the Dorman Long icon have featured in exhibitions, including at the Transporter Bridge Visitor Centre in Middlesbrough, Darlington, and as far afield as Scotland.

To commemorate the 75th anniversary of the Tees Newport Bridge, Dr Jenny Search and Dr Angela Whitecross of the British Steel Archive Project worked with Newport Primary School and Ormesby Secondary School on an anniversary project. The Project's workshops culminated in pupils designing a bench to commemorate the anniversary drawing inspiration from the British Steel Collection held at Teesside Archives. Working with a local forge, the winning design was transformed into a bench that was unveiled at Newport Primary School in May 2009.

The landmark has also featured in the artwork of Brian Collins, Philip Meadows, Alan Morley, Mackenzie Thorpe and Graham Wright, as well as in the work of various photographers including Robin Dale, Richard Wagner and Stuart Wilson. In fact, in 2024 Wilson captured an aerial view of the landmark and used Photoshop to create an image of the main span once again elevated.

David Owst's model on show at the North Eastern Meccano Society Darlington Exhibition, 1985 (North Eastern Meccano Society & Robin Schoolar)

Below: Fred Thompson pictured with his Meccano model at the North Eastern Meccano Society Darlington Exhibition, 2018 (North Eastern Meccano Society & John Witchard)

Caught In The Act, Newport,
Middlesbrough 1970s © Robin Dale,
Mary Evans Picture Library

'Gimme the Moonlight'
(Philip Meadows)

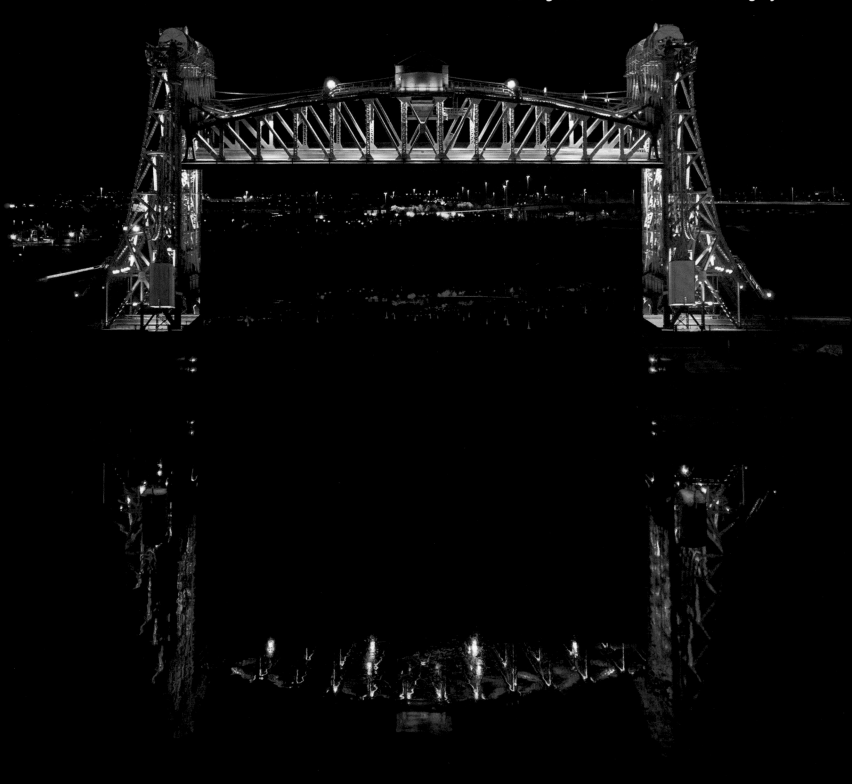

A modern take on the Newport Bridge lifting (Stuart Wilson, Above All Imagery)

Tabloids to Temenos

Returning to the 1990s, as Middlesbrough FC stunned the footballing world in Summer 1996 with the signing of UEFA Champions League winner Fabrizio Ravanelli, the *Daily Mirror* were on hand with a 'Welcome to Middlesbrough' hitlist that informed the Italian and other readers that Middlesbrough was famous for bridges such as the Transporter and Newport Bridges! Beyond the tabloid column inches, Newport Bridge has appeared in a number of fiction and non-fiction works including the novels of Freya North, as well as in Owen Hatherley's 2012 book *A New Kind of Bleak: Journeys Through Urban Britain* in which he contended the artistic work of Dorman Long surpassed that of Anish Kapoor and Cecil Balmond in creating their Temenos sculpture that dominates the skyline at Middlesbrough Dock.

Happy 80th birthday

In 2014, historic photographs from the opening of Newport Bridge 80 years earlier hit the news after their discovery amongst Cleveland Bridge archival records recently transferred to Teesside Archives. Teesside University graduate Jonathon Hooton worked alongside Tosh Warwick and staff to digitise and make accessible a selection of material from the collection. Some of the rarely seen photographs featured in The Green One & The Blue One exhibition, held at the Heritage Gallery in the former Cargo Fleet Iron Company offices, that marked the 80th anniversary of the Newport Bridge and the history of the Transporter Bridge. Opened on the then green bridge's birthday, the exhibition also featured a wide variety of artworks from members of the Cleveland Art Society, itself celebrating 130 years.

Two years later, following ambitions for several years to better illuminate the landmark, work started on a new state-of-the-art new lighting system for the Newport Bridge. Just as local firm Dorman Long built the crossing, local companies were responsible for designing and installing the new lighting system powered by 137 energy efficient lighting units which can be controlled individually or in groups to produce a range of colours or hues. The new lighting system went live in November 2017 and has since done much to draw attention to the Bridge as well as wider cultural and community causes. Notably, as part of the memorial lighting scheme facilities along the Tees, Newport Bridge is illuminated various colours aligned to given causes or events including orange for World Cancer Day, a combination of white, green and purple for International Women's Day, and red and white for St. George's Day.

The new lighting scheme allows the landmark to be illuminated in a variety of colours (Stockton-on-Tees Borough Council)

Heritage and the Steel River

The illumination of the Newport Bridge and a heightened emphasis on celebrating the landmark through cultural and community initiatives reflects shifting, largely positive attitudes towards industrial heritage and long-term efforts to (re)engage people with the River Tees. For decades, local communities had either been excluded from or turned their backs on the Tees owing to a combination of industrial operations and associated restrictions and pollution. Large-scale deindustrialisation along the 'Steel River' since the 1980s has had a devastating impact on heavy industry but also brought emphasis on opening up the waterfront for residential, cultural and leisure activities alongside existing industries. These have included development of the Teesdale Way, Groundwork North East's River Tees Rediscovered programme, new riverside access, waterfront living, the opening of an England Coast Path and new heritage interpretation along the banks of the Tees. As a result, a number of organised events and trails have emerged including the Stockton River Rat Race, Local History Month bike rides, a Tees Heritage Walk complete with a digital element allowing participants to watch footage of Newport Bridge's last lift, and the Huntee digital treasure hunts taking in Teessaurus Park and the Dorman Long landmark.

The Teesdale Way is a popular walking route that takes in the Newport Bridge

Despite new engagement with the Tees and heightened recognition of the importance and value of industrial heritage, the Newport Bridge's 90th birthday was not marked by any official celebrations. The impact of austerity, drastic cuts to local authority budgets, concerns around costly repair of the nearby Transporter Bridge, ongoing maintenance challenges posed by the Newport Bridge, and perhaps even apathy, likely played a part. There was, however, a small amount of local TV and newspaper coverage that drew on the anniversary to reflect on the rich history of the crossing and the continued importance of the Dorman Long-built structure. BBC *Look North* featured interviews with local historians Paul Menzies and Dr Tosh Warwick, whilst both *The Gazette* and *The Northern Echo* featured articles around material uncovered in writing this book.

Industry and the future of the historic bridge

There is still a significant amount of industry along the River Tees and with the development of new, green industries there are lots of opportunities for the twenty-first century waterway to play a major role in the region's economic life.

New commercial and industrial developments around Newport and downriver towards the Transporter Bridge have included the development of the Tees Advanced Manufacturing Park (TeesAMP) on the site of the former Newport Ironworks site in the shadow of the crossing. On the opposite side of the Tees at Port Clarence, Wilton Engineering have emerged as leaders in their sector specialising in designing, manufacturing, coating and loading out large, complicated structures for the Offshore Oil & Gas, Subsea, Marine, Defence, Decommissioning and Offshore Wind industries. By attracting new and expanding industries to the banks of the River Tees, this has potential to share the Tees' history and heritage with new audiences.

Hopefully, the positive changes that have occurred along the Tees combined with future developments enhancing ways in which the river and its landmarks can be maximised for leisure, recreation, culture and community benefit will help ensure more is done to mark the Newport Bridge's centenary in 2034. At present the area faces drastic economic and social challenges, yet there are some reasons for some optimism.

There is huge potential in incorporating the Newport Bridge into future regeneration schemes and waterfront projects. It is a fine example of an industrial heritage attraction – Grade II listed by Historic England – that people can see up close and personal whilst enjoying walks along the river or when en route to other historic offerings on either side of the Tees. For Teesside, landmarks that are record-breaking, world-beating and part of the area's history have lots of potential to instil a sense of place and pride in the past that can be the bedrock of placemaking.

Whilst we are not likely to witness the Tees Newport Bridge lift once again, if the next 90 years can bring wider celebration of the engineering prowess and industrial DNA of Teesside, this can have both an inspirational impact on future generations and help ensure we remember those who helped build and operate this groundbreaking, skyline-defining bridge that was once the envy of the world.

Abigail Warwick, a young visitor to the Newport Bridge in May 2024

Memories of Newport Bridge

As a key part of Teesside life for over 90 years, thousands of Teessiders and visitors alike have memories of the Newport Bridge. Below are a selection of recollections spanning memories of seeing the main span elevated above the Tees, playing near the landmark, working on the iconic structure, and taking artistic inspiration from the Dorman Long bridge.

Childhood and family memories

Elizabeth Al-Anazi: I remember walking along it and turning the wires between the concrete posts and watching hundreds of earwigs scurry out. It was our playground.

Graham Alderson: We lived in Worcester Street and as soon as we were told "the bridge is going up" a gang of us would hot foot it over there to watch it rise and the vessel go through. That would be the highlight of our week!

Nigel Barnbrook: I can honestly say the bridge scared me. When you were down underneath it the water was as black as night, the smell was horrendous and the structure was enormous. But then, I was an eight-year-old at the time!

Thomas Howard Campion: My mother (Olive Campion nee Peacock 1914-2003) lived at 8 Nesham Avenue and worked at the *Gazette* Office. On her way home for dinner she walked past the Newport Bridge opening ceremony, which was still ongoing when she went back to work in the afternoon. Oh well, a bit of family history!

Some of the youngsters who made it to the Newport Bridge's opening ceremony, 1934 (The Northern Echo)

Edward Corner: When we were kids in the 1950s we hid in the girders when it went up!

Steve Driscoll: We'd walk from Parliament Road, cross to the north side and play on the tarzy for hours. I broke my arm and witnessed loads of injuries but it just didn't bother anyone. Great days, laughs and memories.

Eric Oates: I always went over it in the car with Mam, Dad and sister on the way from Thorntree to Sunderland to see Nanna. Invariably the start of a boring journey was wrapped in smog from ICI Billingham and then concluded with the adults jabbering once we got there. Oh, how I wish I could go back just once again and bottle it! Only sis and I left now to reminisce.

Mo Rashid: As kids back in the 1960s we use to live off Cannon Street on Walker Street. Then 10-year-old, me and my friend did stupid things and we would climb up the ladder to the hut at the top and get chased off by the controllers. We thought it was fun but looking back it was very dangerous.

Phil Smith: As a child it was a real treat if my Dad's car was held up in a queue when it operated.

Geoff Taylor: My father Jack Taylor told me that if you had a ship to pilot up to Stockton on a Saturday afternoon, that could make you the most unpopular person on Teesside as the Newport Bridge needed to be raised in good time to allow vessels to transit its span and then sufficient time was needed to lower it before traffic could be allowed through. He said there could be hundreds of cyclists waving their fists and cursing you because your ship's transit meant they were missing the Boro match!

Another colleague, the late Doug Buchan, told of one occasion when he was sailing a vessel from Stockton in the early hours. The ship hoisted the required light signal for the bridge to be raised as it progressed downriver but there was no movement from the bridge. After slowing down as much as possible and with the tide about to start falling, Doug put the ship alongside a jetty upriver of the bridge with just a couple of ropes to hold them fast. Then a young man, he jumped ashore and ran down to the bridge, across the roadway and climbed the vertical ladder to the centre cabin. Sure enough there was the bridge watchkeeper fast asleep. With many expletives delivered, he woke the slumbering man and descended the ladder and ran along the roadway - to his horror as he approached the end of the roadway he realised the bridge was already rising. Now doubly cross and fairly knackered, he retraced his route and with many further expletives advised the unfortunate bridge operator to lower it again and wait until he was off the bridge before raising it again!

Ann Woodgate: Every Sunday afternoon my father took me and my two brothers for a walk over the Tees Bridge so my mother could do the weekly baking in peace. The part over the railway lines was ok but over the river you could see through the cracks on the walkway down to the river and I was terrified. I could hardly breathe until we got past the river. It was no treat to me!

Barbara Whitmore: Great architecture. I lived a stone's throw away and as kids when the bridge raised we would run upstairs to our bedrooms to see the bridge lifting. Amazing!

Andrew Wilson: As a kid I remember playing tigs all over the steelwork, climbing through the steel columns at the road level to access underneath the bridge and along the cable trays above the River Tees – all with not a care in the world.

John Wilson: I loved going over it in my father's car on a regular basis from Norton to go shopping in Middlesbrough.

Working life

Nigel Bythway: I worked on the maintenance of the Newport Bridge between 1987 and 1989. I have got to say it makes the Transporter look like a Meccano kit as this bridge is truly a feat of engineering! l was there on the last lift before they nailed it down for good...it was a sad day but the last lift was still a great sight.

Ron Firby: I was working in Bowes Road the last time it was being lifted and I left work early just to see it - one of the benefits of being a Supervisor!

Rob Harvey: I was working on scaffolding on the bridge back in 1982 and remember when a 16ft scaffold tube dropped from the top of the bridge. We were on the walkway down below and it fell from the top hitting me on the head. I had a fractured skull and got about 60 stitches in my head. You didn't wear hard hats in them days.

Keith Whitaker: For a while I used to attend to the lift when it broke down. Because it wouldn't be working, we had to climb the ladder up the tower to get to the lift room at the top. I also had the privilege of being in the control room when it was operating. Great memories.

An artistic inspiration

Mike Featherstone: In the sixties I remember waiting in the long queues of traffic as the Newport Bridge lifted the road and a ship sailed majestically by. The Transporter and Newport Bridges have that awesome feeling of great British engineering and are an artist's dream outshining many public works of art, the perfect still life. They are a marker of Teesside's identity and symbols of the North East's part in shaping the modern world.

Mike Featherstone's artwork of the Newport Bridge, created to mark the landmark's 80th anniversary

Philip Meadows: I love the 'Dorman Long' cast into the beams. I was on top of Sydney Harbour Bridge on a guided tour and the guide asked people where they were from. When it was my turn I said "Two miles from where this girder was made" pointing to the Dorman Long script. I got the inspiration for my 'Bait Time on the Bridge' artwork from there.

'Bait Time on the Bridge'
by Philip Meadows

Alan Morley: We have two of the biggest Meccano-type bridges on our river and I love to use the Newport Bridge in my invented industrial landscapes artwork. It is a perfect symbolic shape to employ with other mechanical and industrial motifs and is a framework for all sorts of artistic ideas.

Alan Morley, centre, at Newport Bridge with his artwork ahead of the 80th anniversary exhibition

Mona Lisa and a Teesside icon by Alan Morley

Mackenzie Thorpe: I always felt like it was overshadowed by the Transporter, but I have more childhood memories of Newport Bridge. My grandma's house was only a few minutes' walk to it and I remember as a child crossing the bridge to the Stockton side to go swimming. The water was cold, and often a variety of colours, but I remember catching frogs and small fish, taking them home, getting into trouble and then taking them back! Later in life I used to cross Newport Bridge on a bus on my way to work, or walk if I had run out of money. Now when I cross it I feel that strong sense of connection and familiarity...it is like an old friend who watched me grow up.

'Big River' by Mackenzie Thorpe

Abby+Owen: We often find ourselves wandering along the banks of the River Tees, drawn in by the commanding presence of the Newport Bridge. It's more than just a structure; it's a monumental part of our local landscape. Our artwork, which highlights this industrial marvel, was born from a commission rooted in personal admiration. Through the process, our appreciation for the bridge's dramatic stance and its cultural significance to the industrial heritage of our area deepened. We hope it resonates with the same fondness and local pride that it was created with.

Newport Bridge, Middlesbrough by Abby+Owen

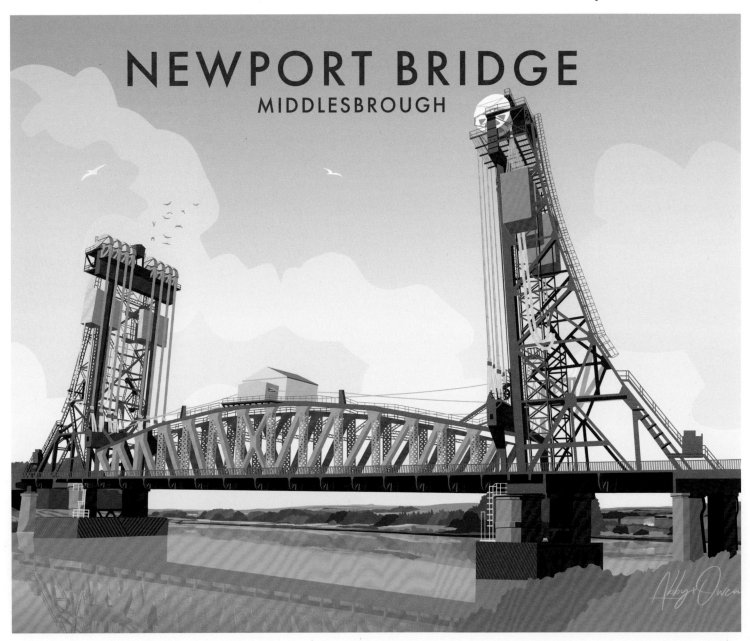

Graham Frank Wright: As a young boy I remember the bridge in operation. The noise it made when lifting the roadway was intense. Watching the ships pass underneath was a sight to behold. I also remember the steam tugs and ships docking at Stockton Wharf. It was a hive of industry in those days. The Newport Lift Bridge in the elevated position inspired me to paint the bridge with the last paddle steam tug leaving the Tees. It is an important part of our industrial heritage.

Graham Frank Wright's artwork depicts the last paddle steam tug passing under Newport Bridge

Selected Bibliography and Further Reading

Collections

British Steel Collection

Teesside Archives

Middlesbrough Libraries

John Severs Collection

Paul Stephenson Collection

Teesside Archives

Yorkshire and North East Film Archive

Newspapers

Billingham & Norton Advertiser

The Daily Mirror

Hartlepool Northern Daily Mail

Middlesbrough Herald & Post

North Eastern Daily Gazette/Evening Gazette

The Northern Echo

The Times

Yorkshire Post and Leeds Mercury

Articles, books and reports

O. Hatherley (2012), A New Kind of Bleak: Journeys Through Urban Britain (Verso: London)

J. Heggie, J. Search et. al. (2011), British Steel Archive Project: Final Report, April 2008-December 2010 (University of Teesside: Middlesbrough)

W. Lillie (1968), The History of Middlesbrough: An Illustration of the Evolution of English Industry (County Borough of Middlesbrough: Portsmouth)

M. Lock et. al. (1947), The County Borough of Middlesbrough Survey and Plan (Middlesbrough Corporation: Yorkshire)

Meccano Magazine (1935), Vol.XX, No. 4, April 1935

Middlesbrough County Borough (1934), Tees Newport Bridge: Official Souvenir Programme (Hood & Co.: Middlesbrough)

C.H. Morris (2000), Bridges Over The Tees (Cleveland Industrial Archaeology Society)

K. Nicholas (1986), The Social Effects of Unemployment in Teesside, 1919-39 (Manchester University Press: Manchester)

P. Stephenson (2019), "This Out of the Way Place": Middlesbrough (Middlesbrough Council: Middlesbrough)

Stockton-on-Tees Borough Council (undated), A History of Tees (Newport) Bridge (Stockton-on-Tees Borough Council: Stockton-on-Tees)

P. Tucker (2024), Teesside's Industrial Landscape (Amberley Publishing: Stroud)

T. Warwick (2011), 'The Politics of Bridge Building: The Long Wait for the Tees (Newport) Bridge', Cleveland History, 99, 37-48

T. Warwick & J. Parker (2016), River Tees: From Source to Sea (Amberley Publishing: Stroud)

M. Williamson, ed. (2008), Life at the ICI: Memories of Working at ICI Billingham (Atkinson Print: Hartlepool)

R. Woodhouse (1991), The River Tees: A North Country River (Terence Dalton: Suffolk)

On The Teapot, Newport, Middlesbrough 1970s
© Robin Dale, Mary Evans Picture Library

'Teesside Sunrise' by Philip Meadows

A modern aerial view of the Dorman Long landmark (Richard Wagner, Wagner Photographic)

The Newport Bridge under construction (Cleveland Bridge Collection, Teesside Archives)

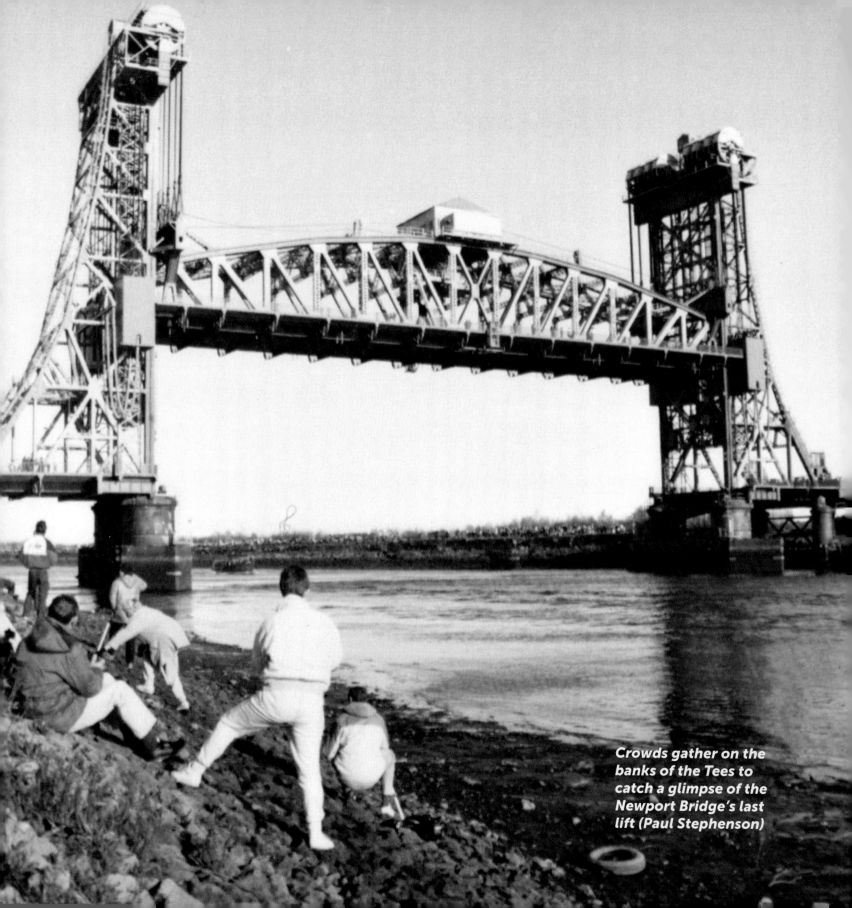

Crowds gather on the banks of the Tees to catch a glimpse of the Newport Bridge's last lift (Paul Stephenson)